The Open University

Science Short Course

Studying Human Nutrition

written by Audrey Brown

SK183 Course Team

Chair	Hilary MacQueen
Author	Audrey Brown
Reader	Peter Morrod
Course Manager	Isla McTaggart
Course Secretary	Jenny Hudson
Project Manager	Rafael Hidalgo
Editor	Margaret Swithenby
Design	Sarah Hofton/Carl Gibbard
Illustration	Sara Hack
Indexing	Jane Henley
External Assessor	Prof. Paul Trayhurn, University of Liverpool

This publication forms part of an Open University course SK183 *Understanding Human Nutrition*. Details of this and other Open University courses can be obtained from the Student Registration and Enquiry Service, The Open University, PO Box 197, Milton Keynes, MK7 6BJ, United Kingdom: tel. +44 (0)870 333 4340, email general-enquiries@open.ac.uk

Alternatively, you may visit the Open University website at http://www.open.ac.uk where you can learn more about the wide range of courses and packs offered at all levels by The Open University.

To purchase a selection of Open University course materials visit http://www.ouw.co.uk, or contact Open University Worldwide, Michael Young Building, Walton Hall, Milton Keynes MK7 6AA, United Kingdom for a brochure. tel. +44 (0)1908 858785; fax +44 (0)1908 858787; email ouwenq@open.ac.uk

The Open University
Walton Hall, Milton Keynes
MK7 6AA

First published 2005. Reprinted with corrections 2006, 2007.

Edited and designed by The Open University.

Typeset by The Open University.

Printed and bound in the United Kingdom by the University Press, Cambridge.

ISBN 0 7492 26983 8

1.3

Contents

Part Three The application of nutritional knowledge

What is nutrition?

1.1 Introduction

During your study of Part One of this course, which covers the first three study periods, called SP1–SP3, you will be working both with this Study Book and with the book *Extracts from Human Nutrition: A health perspective* by Mary Barasi and so you will need to have that book available as you study. It will be referred to here as HN and there will be a 📖 in the margin when you need to read a section from it. Until you are more familiar with studying from that book, you will be asked to read fairly short sections and then return here and continue with this Study Book. It might be useful to put a marker (maybe a small pencil tick) to indicate the end of the part of HN you need to read, so that you don't go on too far. Advice about how to study this course, and study skills in general, is given in cream coloured boxes in this text.

1.2 Definitions of nutrition

Read the first part of HN Chapter 1 called 'Definitions of nutrition' (pp. 3–4). You can ignore the box at the start of each HN chapter. You do not need to make any notes at this stage.

> You will learn best if you read 'actively', that is, if you think about what you are reading. So, as you work through the course, you will find a lot of short questions, indicated by ●, where we would like you to stop and think. The answers follow immediately, marked by ●. You will gain most benefit from these if you cover over our answer while you think about the answer to the question for yourself and maybe re-read the relevant part of the text. In most cases, you do not need to write anything down.

● In what ways has the study of nutrition changed between the start of the 20th century and the start of the 21st?

● The early study of nutrition concentrated on the essential nutrients, how much of each of them was needed, and what were the consequences if the intake was not sufficient. In the second half of the 20th century, it was realised that in many Western counties, where there was apparently no shortage of essential nutrients, there was nevertheless a link between nutrition and a number of important diseases and so the emphasis of research has been to find out those links and encourage people to eat a healthier diet. At the start of the 21st century, the emphasis has begun to move towards 'optimal nutrition', consuming foods that have a positive benefit to heath.

> As you read that short section of HN, you probably met some words whose meaning you did not understand, for example 'biochemical' and 'physiological'. There are various strategies that you can adopt when you come across such new words. You could just read straight past the word, ignoring its detailed meaning, and hope that you can make sense of the rest

of the sentence without it. If you do that, it might be worth underlining the word in pencil, or making a note in the margin, just in case it turns out to be important later. If the word is a non-scientific one, you might look it up in an ordinary dictionary. If it is a scientific one, then try the *Course Glossary*. In this case, the *Glossary* will help you with definitions of 'biochemistry' and 'physiology'. You might also find the index in this book or in HN useful. It could give you other references to the same word, where you might find a better explanation of its meaning.

1.3 Why is nutrition important?

Read the section 'Why is nutrition important' in HN pp. 4–6.

As well as the short 'stop and think' type questions you have already met, there will be some longer questions, like the one that comes next. These questions will take longer to answer and you should try to write out the answer, rather than just thinking about it. You may find it useful to use a (hard-backed) notebook for the answers to these questions, as well as for any other notes that you make as you work through the course, so that everything is kept neatly together. You will be able to check your answers by looking at the answers to these questions at the back of the book. Occasionally, these questions will be based on the Activities or Study Questions in HN (as this one is). However, for the purposes of this course, unless specifically directed to them, you are not expected to do the Activities or Study Questions in HN, though you may find it interesting to read through them.

Question SP1.1   Read through the (fictional) article in HN Activity 1.2 p. 6 and then answer the following questions:

(a) What effect would you expect the article to have if it were published in the UK national newspapers?

(b) What alternative explanations for the findings might there be?

(c) Why might this article be dangerous to the nutrition of readers who took it seriously? ◀

There will also be activities in this Study Book. They will generally take longer to do than the questions and often you will need to work on them over an extended period, as is the case for the one that follows. If answers to the activities are appropriate, they will be at the end of the relevant study period.

Activity SP1.1

You will find it useful for the course, and we hope interesting, to collect information about nutrition, especially nutrition and health, that you come across in newspapers and magazines. You may also find leaflets in doctors' waiting rooms, public libraries, health and fitness centres, etc. Now is the time to set up a folder in which to keep these articles and leaflets. Friends and family might be able to help you to collect a wider range of material. You might like to discuss some of what you find with other SK183 students on the computer conference for the course, as well as with your family and friends. We will be referring to the articles and leaflets again later.

1.4 Collecting information on diet

Read HN pp. 6–11, starting with the section 'What do people eat?' and finishing at the start of 'Studies of nutritional status'. There is no need to make notes but if you come across things that you do not understand – for example, the data on energy intake and expenditure, and the units in which energy is measured – then put a mark in the margin of HN, so that you can come back to those points later, when they have been explained.

● What is a 'staple' food and how does its role in the diet differ between poorer and richer countries?

● In most modern populations, a staple food is usually a type of cereal (such as wheat flour or rice) or a root (such as cassava) or tuber (such as potato). In poorer countries, the staple food makes up a larger proportion of the diet than it does in richer countries where a wider range of foods is available.

Question SP1.2   Referring back to the sections you have just read in HN as necessary, list the main ways (two or three for each) in which data about food intake can be collected for (a) populations, (b) families and (c) individuals, noting any problems with the methods. ◀

1.5 Nutritional status

In this section, you will need to use a calculator for some basic arithmetic. If you are not familiar with using a calculator, you should now read the relevant sections on using a calculator, decimal numbers and scientific units, in the *Maths Skills Booklet*.

An approximate measure of whether an adult is over or under the ideal weight for their height can be expressed as a single value based on their weight and their height. The value is called the body mass index (BMI). The following formula is used to calculate BMI:

$$\text{BMI} = \frac{\text{weight in kg}}{(\text{height in m})^2}$$

The term (height in m)^2 means that you multiply the person's height in metres (m) – say 1.80 m – by itself, that is 1.80 m × 1.80 m, which gives 3.24 m^2. The unit m^2 (square metres) normally describes an area (see *Maths Skills Booklet*). However, here we are only concerned with the numerical value of the answer; it has no meaning in terms, for example, of the area of the person's body surface. This particular formula is used simply because experience shows that it gives the best measure of this aspect of a person's nutritional status.

Some people know their weight in stones and pounds, and their height in feet and inches. In this case, the values must be first converted into kilograms (kg) and m respectively. To do the conversion, you need the following information:

1 stone = 6.35 kg

1 pound (lb) = 0.45 kg

1 foot (ft) = 0.305 m

1 inch = 0.025 m

Question SP1.3 A woman weighs 10 stone 6 lbs and her height is 5 ft 9 inches.

(a) What are her weight and height in kg and m respectively? You should give your answers to the nearest whole kg and to the nearest centimetre (cm) (0.01 m).

(b) What is her BMI? Use the information at the top of HN p. 12 to identify whether her BMI falls within the desirable range. ◀

Read quickly through the remainder of HN Chapter 1 from the bottom of p. 11 to the end of p. 15. You should realise that BMI is not the only anthropometric indicator of nutritional status, but you do not need to understand the details of the other methods at this stage. You will also learn much more about the biochemical indicators later, so again, you only need to be aware that analysis of various aspects of the body chemistry can also be used as a measure of nutritional status. Similarly, you do not need to be concerned about any details in the remainder of the chapter, and you can ignore the Summary, Study Questions and References and Further Reading on pp. 16–17.

1.6 The biology of cells

To understand more about nutrition, you need some basic biological background. If you have studied biology before, you will probably be able to skip through the remainder of SP1 quite quickly, just refreshing your memory about any parts that you have forgotten. Since the sections of text on a cream background contain advice about studying and study techniques, you will find it useful to read carefully through those, even if the biology is familiar.

All living things are made up of small subunits called cells. There are about 100 trillion (100 000 000 000 000) cells in the adult human body, though estimates vary considerably. Nearly all cells are much too small to be seen with the naked eye; in fact 100 human skin cells laid end to end would stretch for only 1 millimetre (1 mm). Figure SP1.1 shows drawings of a range different types of human cells.

When you meet a new diagram, there are three things you need to study. You should first read the caption, the wording that tells you what the diagram is about. Then quickly look over the diagram to get an overall impression and finally work carefully through the labels, checking the parts of the drawing to which they relate. Sometimes the label will be on one side of the drawing and sometimes on the other, simply to use the limited space more efficiently. To avoid confusion, the labelling lines do not overlap. In this course, you will meet a number of different sorts of diagram and you will be given advice on how to 'read' them whenever you meet a new type. Don't worry if the initial impression is complicated; working through diagrams step by step will enable you to understand their meaning.

In Figure SP1.1, you will see that the cells differ considerably according to their particular function in the body. Skin cells (Figure SP1.1a) are closely packed together and form a protective layer over the body surface. The cells lining the digestive system (Figure SP1.1b) have a 'ruffled' edge which helps them to absorb the products of the breakdown of food. Nerve cells, like the one in Figure SP1.1c, have an irregular shape, as they fit between other cells, and some have elongated branches to transmit information to other cells in the body. Muscle cells (Figure SP1.1d) contain filaments that can contract, causing the cell to change its shape and generate a force on the bones of the skeleton, so that movement can occur.

● Using Figure SP1.1, identify those features that are common to all these cells.

● They all have a cell membrane round the outside, and cytoplasm and a nucleus inside.

In fact, there are a lot of other common features inside cells, within the cytoplasm, but they are too small to be shown in drawings at this scale. The cell membrane encloses the cell, whatever its shape, and it has a vital role in taking up or excluding selected chemicals. The cytoplasm is the site of most of the chemical processes that go on in the cell, which together are termed the cell's metabolism. The term 'metabolism' is also used as a general description of all of the chemical processes that go on throughout the body.

All the cells in our body have been made from one original cell, a fertilised egg. This cell divides into two, then each one of those divides to give four, then again to give eight, and so on. Continued cell division ultimately gives rise to the enormous numbers of cells present in an adult body. Some cells, such as nerve cells, lose the ability to divide once they are mature, whereas others, known as stem cells, continue to divide throughout life to replace old or damaged cells of a particular type. Cells in the bone marrow that produce blood cells are a type of stem cell.

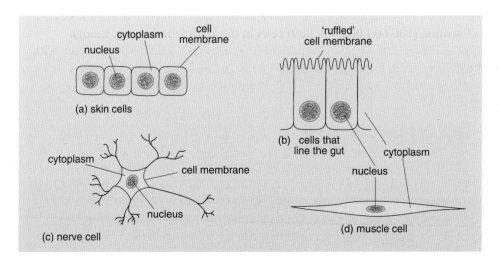

Figure SP1.1 Drawings of a selection of human cell types. (a) Skin cells. (b) Cells that line the gut. (c) Nerve cell. (d) Muscle cell. These cells are not all drawn to the same scale.

The code that enables the cell to make all of its components is carried by a molecule called DNA (deoxyribonucleic acid), almost all of which is within the chromosomes in the nucleus. So each time a cell divides, a copy of this code must be produced, so that each of the two new cells has a complete set of DNA. The chromosomes are only visible in the cell when it is undergoing division, as shown in Figure SP1.2.

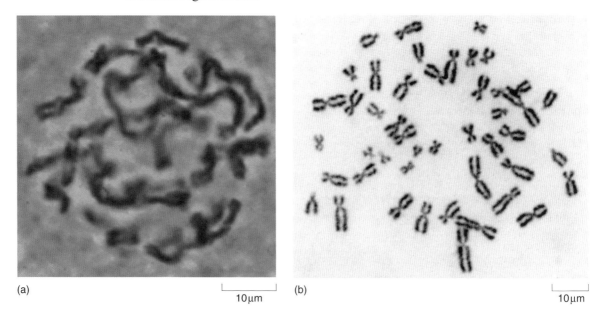

(a) 10 μm (b) 10 μm

Figure SP1.2   (a) Chromosomes from a white blood cell as seen at the beginning of cell division. (b) The same chromosomes spread out so that they are all visible. The chromosomes have been stained with a special dye to make them more easily visible using a laboratory microscope. One micrometre (μm) is one thousandth of a millimetre.

Most cells cluster together with other similar ones to make a tissue. For example, muscle tissue is made up of many millions of muscle cells (Figure SP1.1d), all working together. The organs in the body, such as liver, kidney and heart, consist of more than one type of tissue. The wall of the small intestine, for example, consists not only of the cells shown in Figure SP1.1b, but also of several other types of cell. There are cells whose function is to produce and release enzymes, chemicals that are needed to digest food. There are muscle cells which cause food to be moved along the intestine, nerve cells which coordinate gut activity and a large number of tiny blood vessels into which the digested food is absorbed.

Personal glossary: Although we have provided a *Glossary* for this course, you may find it useful to create your own 'personal glossary'. This has two main advantages over the formal *Course Glossary* in terms of your own learning. First, the process of choosing which, if any, words to include from a particular section helps you to identify the important points from that section and second, thinking about definitions and writing them in your own words will help you to remember them better, and you will be able to find them again quickly if you need to check up on them later. There are a number of ways of laying out your glossary. In choosing the best way for you, you might like to bear these points in mind:

- Your glossary will be easiest to use if it is arranged, at least approximately, in alphabetical order.

- You don't know in advance how many words there will be.

- You may want your glossary to be 'portable' so that you can have it with you whenever and wherever you are studying.

Possible solutions are:

- A small notebook, which you can divide up by the letter of the alphabet.

- An address book, or similar, which is already divided by letter.

- A loose-leaf binder with a page for each letter, to which more can be added if needed.

- File cards in a small box.

- A database package on your computer.

There is, of course, a trade-off between, on the one hand, perfect alphabetical order and hence ease of searching (in which the computer wins easily) and, on the other hand, convenience, when a small notebook or address book is probably the best. Finally, don't spend time setting up a very elaborate system at first, until you are sure that you will use it.

1.7   The blood system

There are two types of large blood vessels. Arteries carry blood away from the heart, and then branch many times, eventually forming tiny vessels called capillaries. The capillaries join up again, and the blood returns to the heart in the other large blood vessels, the veins. The products of digestion of food are absorbed into the capillaries and so carried round to wherever they are needed in the body. Blood capillaries in the lungs pick up oxygen from the air that is breathed in, and the oxygenated blood can then also be supplied to all the cells of the body. Digested food and oxygen are used in the metabolic processes of all cells.

Blood consists of a liquid called plasma (or serum) and two main types of cell, white cells and red cells. White cells, whose chromosomes you saw in Figure SP1.2, provide the body with its immune system which detects and destroys foreign material, especially bacteria and viruses.

We are not able to look at the chromosomes of the other type, red blood cells, because, when they are mature, they lose their nucleus containing the chromosomes.

● What effects might the loss of the chromosomes have on a cell?

◉ Earlier you read that the DNA in the chromosomes carries the code that enables a cell to make all its components and to pass that information on to other cells when the cell divides. So, without a nucleus, you might predict that the cell is unable to make any new components, or repair damaged ones, and it cannot divide because it has no chromosomes to pass on.

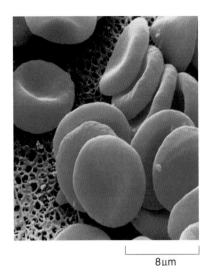

8 μm

Figure SP1.3 A photograph of red blood cells.

This lack of chromosomes means that mature red blood cells have a limited lifespan in the body (about 120 days), and must be replaced by new ones made in the bone marrow. Red blood cells are an unusual shape, discs with dents on each side, as shown in Figure SP1.3. There are about five million red blood cells in a cubic millimetre (mm^3) of blood. 1 mm^3 is a cube with sides 1 mm long, the size of a tiny drop of blood. The red colour of blood is due to a substance in the red blood cells called haemoglobin, which contains iron. Molecules of haemoglobin pick up the oxygen in the lungs and release it again to cells elsewhere in the body.

This section completes your study of SP1. It ends, as do all the study periods, with a brief summary of the main points that have been covered. You should read through these points carefully, checking that you are familiar with their contents. If you are not, then now would be a good time to re-read the relevant parts before you begin SP2.

Summary of SP1

1   Nutrition can be defined in various different ways and study of it is of interest to many groups of people.

2   There are various ways of measuring what people eat, and there are advantages and disadvantages to all the methods.

3   One measure of whether an adult is overweight or underweight is to calculate their body mass index (BMI) which can then be compared with typical ranges for the population.

4   Other body measurements (anthropometric indicators), as well as biochemical and clinical (medical) indicators, can also be used to determine a person's nutritional status.

5   Nutritional information is used to study the links between diet and health, and to provide dietary advice to minimise the risks of disease.

6   The human body is made up of cells, which are surrounded by a cell membrane and contain cytoplasm and, usually, a nucleus.

7   There are many types of cell in the human body, each specialised to carry out a particular function

8   Blood circulates round the body through arteries, capillaries and veins, and transports digested food and supplies oxygen to all the cells of the body.

9   White blood cells provide the body with its immune system, to destroy foreign material that gets into the body.

10 Red blood cells, which have no nucleus, contain haemoglobin which carries oxygen around the body.

What are the influences on eating habits?

2.1 Major nutrients

This study period starts by briefly describing the main types of nutrient present in food and then introduces the parts of the human digestive system as a background to working through HN Chapter 2.

Nutritional Information				
○ Typical value per 100g			● 40g serving with 125ml of semi-skimmed milk	
ENERGY	1501 kJ 355 kcal		852 kJ 201 kcal	
PROTEIN	8g		8g	
CARBOHYDRATES	69g		34g	
of which sugars	25g		16g	
starch	44g		18g	
FAT	5g		4g	
of which saturates	5g		2.5g	
FIBRE	9g		3.5g	
SODIUM	0.55g		0.3g	
VITAMINS:		(%RDA)		(%RDA)
THIAMIN (B$_1$)	0.9 mg	(65)	0.4 mg	(30)
RIBOFLAVIN (B$_2$)	1 mg	(65)	0.6 mg	(40)
NIACIN	11.3 mg	(65)	4.6 mg	(25)
VITAMIN B$_6$	1.3 mg	(65)	0.6 mg	(30)
FOLIC ACID	250 µg	(125)	110 µg	(55)
VITAMIN B$_{12}$	0.65 µg	(65)	0.75 µg	(75)
MINERALS:				
IRON	8.8 mg	(65)	3.6 mg	(25)

Figure SP2.1   Nutritional information from a packet of breakfast cereal.

● Look at the nutritional information on the label in Figure SP2.1. What are the three main types of nutrient?

● In the UK, the nutritional information is always given in the same order. Firstly, it gives the energy in the food. Then the three main types of nutrient are listed – protein, carbohydrates and fat. More details are sometimes given about the types of carbohydrate and fat present.

These three main types of nutrient – protein, carbohydrates and fat – are known as macronutrients, because they are needed in the body in relatively large quantities (macro- indicates 'large'), while vitamins and minerals, which the body needs in much smaller amounts, are referred to as micronutrients (micro- is 'small', as in words like 'microscope'). It is the macronutrients which are digested as they pass through the gut, into smaller, simpler molecules which can pass through the wall of the small intestine into the bloodstream and thus be carried around the body. These simpler molecules can then be used by the body for energy and to build up and repair structures within the body, as we will see later. Many of the micronutrients can be absorbed unchanged into the blood from the intestine.

2.2   The human digestive system

Humans have been likened to doughnuts – a body with a hole through the middle! The digestive tract, also referred to biologically as the gut, is essentially a long tube, running between the mouth and the anus. In the average adult, it measures 4.5 metres in length.

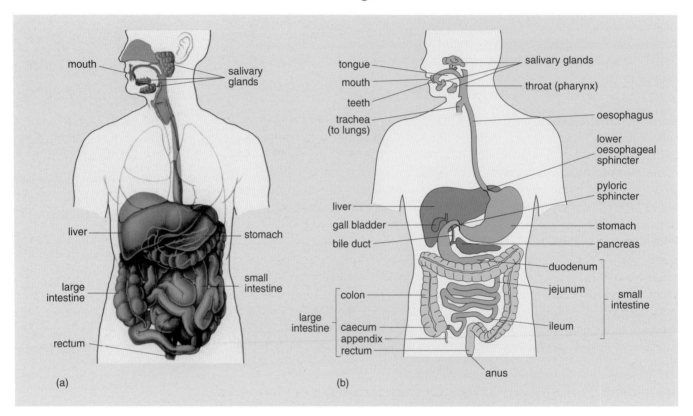

Figure SP2.2   Anatomy of the digestive tract (gut) and associated organs. (a) View of some internal organs with overlying bone and other tissue removed. (The structures shown in outline on either side of the oesophagus are the lungs.) (b) Simplified diagram of the gut and associated organs.

Spend a few moments looking at Figure SP2.2, reading the caption and all the labels. As you can see in Figure SP2.2a, the internal organs are packed very closely together inside the body, so to show the details, they have to be separated and shown relatively smaller, as in Figure SP2.2b. In the mouth, the food is chewed and lubricated with saliva, produced by the salivary glands, which moistens and softens it, and starts the process of digestion. The pieces of food are swallowed, passing through the throat (pharynx) and down the oesophagus into the stomach. There are muscles called sphincters controlling the entry to and exit from the stomach.

● From Figure SP2.2b, what are the names of the two sphincters?

● The one at the lower end of the oesophagus is, not surprisingly, called the lower oesophageal sphincter and the one at the exit of the stomach is called the pyloric sphincter.

The stomach is a bag-like organ, where digestive enzymes and acid are added to the food and where the first major digestion and mixing processes occur. The partly digested food then passes into the small intestine which is the longest part of the gut and is where most of the digestion occurs. Some digestive secretions enter the small intestine from the pancreas and liver, while others are produced by the cells lining the inside of the small intestine itself. So, during its passage along the digestive system, the food is broken down both physically into smaller pieces, and chemically, by enzymes, so that the large molecules in the food are broken down into smaller ones (you will learn more about this later), which can then be absorbed into the bloodstream. The digestion and absorption take place mostly in the first two parts of the small intestine (the duodenum and the jejunum); the last part (the ileum) provides reserve capacity.

From the small intestine, the remains of the food pass into a wider section of the tube, called the large intestine or bowel. The first part of the large intestine is called the caecum, which is a pouch-like structure from which the very narrow appendix protrudes. The caecum merges with the major region of the large intestine known as the colon. (Sometimes the term 'colon' is used to describe the entire large intestine.) It is here in the large intestine that vitamins and minerals are absorbed, together with most of the water. The digestive secretions have added more water to that taken in as drinks and in food, making the gut contents quite runny. The absorption of the water concentrates the remains of the undigested food into a semi-solid mass called faeces. The colon is also home to many beneficial bacteria, which break down some of the food, especially plant materials, which otherwise could not be digested. Up to half the dry weight of faeces is made up of living and dead bacteria. The last region of the large intestine is the rectum, in which the faeces remain until they are expelled through the anus.

Question SP2.1   On the basis of what you have just read, identify which of the following statements about human digestion are correct and which are false. Then write a correct version of each of the false statements.

(a) Bacteria in the stomach help with digestion of plant material.

(b) The liver releases its secretions into the small intestine.

(c) Water and minerals are absorbed in the large intestine.

(d) Enzymes are released from the wall of the large intestine and digest the food.

(e) More than 50% of the dry weight of the faeces is made up of bacteria. ◀

Question SP2.2   (a) What are the three macronutrient groups and the two micronutrient groups?

(b) List the main parts of the digestive system that food passes through after it enters the mouth. ◀

2.3 Reasons for eating

With that background, you are now ready to start working though HN Chapter 2. Again, you will be advised to read it through in small sections, returning to this text after each one. Before you go any further, you might like to try HN Activity 2.1 p. 18, which asks you to think about your own eating habits.

 Now read through Question SP2.3 below and then read HN from p. 18 to the top of p. 19 up to the start of 'Reasons for eating'.

Question SP2.3   Make a list of at least five reasons given in that short section of HN, to answer the question 'Why do we eat?'   ◀

> You probably noticed that because you were looking for the answer to this question, you concentrated more on the text than you would have done if you had been just asked to read the section. The importance of active reading is one of the main reasons for making notes. We'll be coming back to that later in SP2.

Now look at the bottom half of HN p. 19. You should recognise HN Figure 2.1 as a representation of the human digestive system although it differs slightly from Figure SP2.2. Now, in pencil, and using the same style as in Figure SP2.2, label the following items on HN Figure 2.1 p. 19: salivary glands, oesophagus, stomach, liver, small intestine and large intestine. Try not to let the labelling lines overlap with each other or with the lines on HN Figure 2.1.

As well as illustrating the digestive tract, HN Figure 2.1 also summarises some of the factors controlling hunger and food intake. This diagram is one of the most complex you will need to deal with in the course, so don't worry if you find it difficult. Some of the main points are summarised here. After you have read each point, write its number at the appropriate place on the diagram.

1   This person imagines a slice of chocolate cake. These thoughts are generated in the brain ('cephalic' means 'of the head') and the person feels hungry, indicated by a plus sign between the cake and the word 'Hunger' in the brain. Write '1' beside 'Sight, smell or even the thought of food …'.

2   The person may see or smell food, which also stimulates the brain, as shown by the 'plus' signs in the 'Sight' and 'Smell' circles, making them feel hungry. Write '2' beside the plate of food.

3   Any one of these three factors, thought of food, sight of food and smell of food, when recognised by the brain, triggers the secretion of saliva in the mouth and gastric juices in the stomach ('gastric' means 'of the stomach'). You will almost certainly be familiar with the sensation of your 'mouth watering' under similar circumstances and your 'stomach rumbling' when you are hungry. Write '3' beside 'Secretion of saliva and gastric juices'.

4   Now let us assume that the person eats some food, shown shaded in the stomach in HN Figure 2.1. The food causes the stomach to be stretched from its 'empty' condition. The stretching is detected by special nerves in the stomach wall (called 'stretch receptors'), which send nerve impulses to the brain. These signals are perceived by the brain and eventually are translated into thoughts like 'I'm full'. That is indicated by the minus sign in the arrow between 'Gastric distension detected by stretch receptors' and the brain. Write '4' beside 'Gastric distension detected by stretch receptors'.

5   The food passes on into the small intestine, where a small amount of food is shown as a shaded blob. The presence of food there causes the release of gut hormones. Hormones are chemicals released from cells into the blood, which carries them round the body so that they can have effects at some distance from where they are produced. In this case, the hormone CCK (cholecystokinin) is produced by cells in the wall of the small intestine and has its effect on the brain. Again you can see a 'minus' sign on the arrow, indicating that CCK's effect is to reduce the feelings of hunger and increase feelings of 'fullness' ('satiety', pronounced 'sat–eye–ity'). Write '5' beside 'Presence of food in duodenum …'.

6   When the food has been digested, the products of digestion are absorbed into the blood, through the wall of the small intestine. Two of the important products of digestion are glucose, from the digestion of carbohydrates, and amino acids, from the digestion of protein. (You will learn more about these molecules later.) The rise in the amounts of these substances in the blood is indicated in HN Figure 2.1 by an upward pointing arrow ' ↑ Glucose and amino acids'. Write '6' beside 'Absorption …'.

●   What is the effect on the brain of an increase in the absorption of glucose and amino acids?

◐   The arrow leading to the brain has a minus sign on it, indicating a negative effect on the hunger centres of the brain. When food has been digested and the products absorbed, the person feels less hungry.

●   What is the relationship between fat absorption and hunger?

◐   The statement in brackets following the information on glucose and amino acid absorption indicates that when there is an increase (↑) in fat absorption, there is no reduction in the feelings of hunger.

> The use of plus and minus signs in a diagram to indicate positive or negative effects is a common scientific shorthand, as are upward pointing arrows to mean 'increase' and downward pointing arrows to mean 'decrease'. You will need to be able to recognise their meaning when you meet them in other contexts.

The text relating to this diagram (HN pp.19–21) is quite complex and you do not need to read it.

2.4   More reasons for eating

Start reading again at 'Habit as an influence on eating behaviour', towards the end of HN p. 21 and read up to the middle of p. 23, stopping before the section called 'Sensory appeal'. Just read through the text once, and then return here.

> You now need to consider how you are going to locate information that you have already read when you need to find it again. When you get further on in your study, you might need to check up on something that you remember reading about earlier, perhaps to answer a question or as a reminder of the meaning of a word or, when you get to the end of the course, you might need to find some information when you are completing the course assessment. So it is important to develop some way of finding information again quickly. There are two main ways of doing this – by making notes or by highlighting in the text. The next sections give you a chance to practise both and see which works best for you.

Making notes: It is important not to make too many notes, to avoid overburdening yourself with a system that you cannot continue and which fades away to nothing after a few study sessions. As already suggested, it is best to make your notes in a book, rather than on odd bits of paper which are likely to get lost. Your notes are purely for your own benefit and do not need to be read by anyone else, though you do have to be able to read them yourself at a later stage! But they can contain abbreviations that only you understand and they don't have to be written as complete sentences.

Activity SP2.1

Re-read the three short sections on HN pp. 21–23, making yourself some notes as a reminder of the main points covered. Compare your notes with those in the answer to this activity at the end of this study period.

Your notes may have been very different from the ones given in the answer and it would be useful to spend a moment thinking about the differences. There are many styles of note-making and yours may be entirely as good as the example, and probably better for you. The important activity is the process of making the notes, rather than the style or form of the notes that you have made. In order to make the notes, you have to interact with the material and that helps you to process the information, which helps with your understanding and later recall of the content. You can see that headings are included in these notes. The headings enable the notes to be linked quickly to the relevant part of the text. It might be useful to write down the page numbers too. You may have written considerably longer notes than the examples. If so, consider whether everything you have included is essential, since, as mentioned earlier, if the notes take too long to make, you may get bored and also may find that your studying is taking too long. The notes should just remind you of the main points in the section; you can always go back and check up on the details later. You may also have noticed that these notes are not just phrases copied from the book. Trying to write them in your own words helps you to process and later recall the information.

Now go on to read the sections 'Sensory appeal' and 'Social influence' (HN pp. 23–25). Just read them once and then return here.

An alternative to making notes is to highlight the important words in the text.

Highlighting: You may choose to use a special 'highlighter' pen on the text, or you could underline words with pen or pencil. Whichever you use, you must be very selective in choosing the words to mark, so again this method requires active reading and understanding first. Remember that both this Study Book and the HN book are yours to be used in your learning; they do not have to be returned to the OU. So you should be prepared to write in them and use them in the way that is most useful to you.

● Re-read the 'Sensory appeal' and 'Social influence' sections and choose up to about 5 words in each paragraph to highlight. Compare your chosen words with those given here.

● Numbering the paragraphs 1–7 in 'Sensory appeal', and 8–10 in 'Social influence', here are some words you might have chosen:

paragraph 1: appearance – smell – taste – texture

paragraph 2: visual – expectations – appearance – colorants – 'natural' colour

paragraph 3: smell and taste interact – taste buds

paragraph 4: children – sweet – energy-dense – bitter – pregnant – cancer – zinc

paragraph 5: feel – temperature – pain – anaesthetic

paragraph 6: 'bliss points'

paragraph 7: variety – intake greater – wine – social – monotony

paragraph 8: hospitality – visitors

paragraph 9: wasting

paragraph 10: – (no words highlighted)

> You may have chosen quite different words from those listed here, but the important thing is that they are sufficient to remind you of the main points in that paragraph. If you don't set yourself a limit on the number of words you highlight, then you risk highlighting whole sentences, or even whole paragraphs and, of course, if you are looking back to find something and the whole paragraph is highlighted, you will have to read the whole paragraph again, rather than just the key words.
>
> Now that you have experimented with both methods, decide which you are going to use for the rest of this study period. You may need more practice yet to decide which will be the best for you in the long term. Some students use a mix of note-making and highlighting; others use exclusively one or the other.

You will notice (paragraph 10) that the author of HN has summarised many of the points from this part of the chapter in the form of a diagram, HN Figure 2.5 p. 25. Devising diagrams of this sort yourself can be time-consuming, but they are a useful way of showing links between various items. You will find it useful to work through these summary diagrams when you meet them in HN.

2.5 Food habits

> You will often find it useful to read through sections of the HN book twice. On the first fairly quick read through you should aim to get an idea of the main points and the overall picture. If there are questions in this Study Book on a particular section, you might find it useful to read through those too, so that during the second reading, you can make relevant notes or highlight relevant points, knowing the overall context.

Read 'Food habits', from p. 25 as far as 'Food choices' towards the end of p. 27, making notes or highlighting important words. Then answer Question SP2.4, using your notes or highlighting to help you to pinpoint the information from HN quickly.

Question SP2.4   You should not need to write more than two or three sentences in answer to each of parts (a)–(d).

(a) How do the main influences on the food habits of a child change when they go to school?

(b) Why are families now less likely to eat their meals together?

(c) How might the magazines read by teenage girls affect their diet and eating habits?

(d) Amongst which groups in the population are changes towards healthy living least likely to be found? ◀

> Studying an Open University course can be a rather solitary activity, but most students find that their understanding is significantly improved if they talk about the material they are studying with others. The material in this course is particularly suited to discussions with friends and family. At this point you might, for example, like to discuss HN Activity 2.2 on p. 26 with others, to get their views on the question 'Why do we eat?'.

2.6   Food choices

Now complete your reading of Chapter 2 from 'Food choices' p. 27 to the end on p. 34. You should make notes, or highlight words, as you read and then use those to answer the following questions. If you have selected the most important information, you should be able to answer most of Questions SP2.5 and SP2.6 without re-reading the whole text.

Question SP2.5   (a) What are the two main factors that determine food choice?

(b) Why do residents of rural areas in developing countries generally have a smaller range of foods than those who live in large cities?

(c) List the aspects of food availability that are controlled by legislation.

(d) What percentage of their budget does the average British person spend on food? ◀

Question SP2.6   (a) What are the five groups generally used to categorise food in the UK and other Western countries? Beside each of the five groups, write whether they would be categorised as a core food, a secondary food or a peripheral food.

(b) Why do hospitals often provide a choice of menus for their patients?

(c) What reasons are given for the adoption of a vegetarian diet?

(d) Why do married men in general have healthier diets than single men?

> While reading this chapter in HN, you will have met some references to other works, e.g. DEFRA, 2001 and Wilding, J. P., 2002. The details of the references are given at the end of the chapter (pp. 34–35). They are listed in alphabetical order of the first author and the year of publication is always given as an extra way of identifying the particular reference. Some references include the Latin phrase 'et al.' which is short for '*et alia*',

meaning 'and others', telling you that more authors than those listed were involved in the work. There is no need, during this course, to access any of these references, but if you have an interest in a particular article or book, you may be able to obtain it through the Open University Library, which you can access through your StudentHome web page.

Summary of SP2

1   The main nutrients or macronutrients are protein, carbohydrate and fat.

2   After eating, food passes through the digestive system (gut) where it is broken down physically, and chemically by digestive enzymes into simpler molecules which are then absorbed into the bloodstream.

3   There are many reasons why people eat, including: hunger; because it is a mealtime (habit); for psychological reasons, such as pleasure, comfort, etc.; because food tastes and smells good; and for social reasons.

4   Each of us develops certain food habits at an early age, which can change throughout life in response to information from sources such as cookery books, TV programmes and nutrition educators and the influence of other people (family and friends).

5   Food choice is dependent on availability and acceptability.

Answer to Activity SP 2.1

Here are some notes on these sections:

Habit as an influence on eating behaviour

3 meals/day not essential – but too much snacking may upset eating regulation.

What is the difference between meals and snacks?

Snack = one type of food, eaten informally. Snacks may or may not be good nutritionally. Meals usually have mix of foods, and take time to prepare/eat – often better mix of nutrients than snacks. Times of meals important in society, but perhaps not for babies. People may ignore hunger cues – can result in overeating or compulsive dieting.

Psychological need

People eat when bored, depressed, anxious – as comfort. People can reject food deliberately – to express anger, cause hurt to others, etc.

Basics of a healthy diet

3.1 Introduction

In this study period, you will be reading HN Chapter 3, making notes or highlighting as you prefer. You might like to read through the whole chapter first, then come back and answer the questions here, or you may prefer to work through it in small sections, as suggested here, answering the questions as you go along.

Later in this study period, you will need to know your food intake during a typical day, to answer Activity SP3.1. On a convenient day, you should make a list of the food you eat, following the example on the left-hand side of HN p. 50 Figure 3.6.

3.2 What to eat and how much

Read the start of HN Chapter 3 from p. 36 to the start of 'What are the features of a healthy diet?' on p. 38.

Question SP3.1   Explain the meaning of the following sentence in your own words: 'Epidemiological evidence does, however, support the view that diets based largely on plant foods are most associated with health and longevity, where food supplies are adequate.' (p. 36, second column).

● Spend a few moments thinking about what you consider to be a 'normal' portion of some foods. For example, you might consider: breakfast cereal, sandwiches, fruit, yoghurt, steak, chips and cheese. If you have the opportunity, ask someone else to do the same exercise and compare their answers with your own.

● For some foods, a portion is determined by the food itself. So, an apple or a banana would be a portion. However, for grapes a portion might be a handful. For other foods, the size of a portion is determined by the food producer. Yoghurt is a good example, where most people would consider that one 125 g pot of yoghurt constitutes a portion. On packets of breakfast cereal, the size of a portion is often indicated on the pack with the nutritional information. For example, it may give the nutritional content of a '40 g serving' (see Figure SP2.1), but how many consumers actually weigh out 40 g of breakfast cereal and how many just pour out what they consider to be a 'normal' bowlful and have no idea of the weight of cereal they have chosen? If you eat sandwiches at lunchtime, would you consider one round of sandwiches (made with two slices of bread, and filling) to be sufficient? Pre-packed sandwiches normally contain one round. Restaurants often offer steaks in hugely different portion sizes for customers with different appetites. Similarly, a portion of chips means very different things to different people. And if you finish a meal with cheese, that can mean anything from a small pre-packed piece of Cheddar to a large piece of Camembert or perhaps chunks of several varieties of cheese from a cheeseboard. You should bear considerations like this in mind when considering nutritional advice; what one person considers to be a 'portion' could be very different from someone else's viewpoint.

3.3 A healthy diet

Now read HN 'What are the features of a 'healthy' diet?' from p. 38 to the end of p. 40.

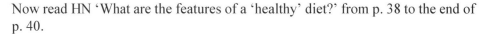

● How has the understanding of what is meant by a 'balanced diet' changed over the last 50 years?

◐ 50 years ago, the emphasis was on making sure that people had sufficient of the macronutrients (protein, carbohydrate and fat) to maintain their body weight and, in children, their growth rate. This priority was probably because it followed a time of 'food rationing' during World War II, when people, especially children, might have been short of the basic nutrients, particularly protein. It was assumed, probably correctly at the time, that a sufficient intake of macronutrients would also ensure a sufficient intake of micronutrients. Now that (at least in Western Europe) few people are actually short of food, the emphasis has changed to one of concern about the intake of appropriate amounts of both macronutrients and micronutrients (minerals and vitamins).

Question SP3.2 Compare the dietary guidelines currently available in the UK and the USA by making a list of those that appear in both, those that appear only in the UK list and those that appear only in the USA list. Comment briefly on the comparisons. ◀

3.4 Nutritional requirements

Read 'What nutrients are needed and in what amounts?' HN p. 41 as far as half-way down the first column of p. 42.

Question SP3.3 Write a definition of the 'physiological nutrient requirement' in a single sentence. List any concerns and problems with this definition as a series of bullet points. ◀

● Describe in your own words, the way in which HN Figure 3.1 illustrates the ideas of nutrient intake and deficiency, by describing what is represented by each item in the sketches.

◐ The water in the sink represents the store of a particular nutrient. The water coming in when the tap is turned on represents the intake of that nutrient in the diet and the water running away down the plughole represents the using-up of the nutrient by the body. The first drawing shows a sink full of water, representing a full (replete) store of the nutrient, with the tap turned on keeping it topped up, and the nutrient trickling away down the plughole as it is being used up by the body. In the second drawing, the intake of nutrient is low – the tap is only adding a small amount of water to the sink. As the nutrient continues to trickle away, the stores of the nutrient (amount of water in the sink) are beginning to decline. In the third drawing, there is no intake of this particular nutrient (the tap is turned off) and, as the nutrient continues to be used by the body, the stores (level in the sink) become very low. Finally, in the fourth drawing, the nutrient stores are completely depleted and the person is likely to show signs of clinical deficiency. It is important to note that such deficiency is not detectable until this very late stage.

3.5 Nutrition in a population

You will meet some graphs in this section. If you are not familiar with reading information from graphs, you should now work through the relevant sections in the *Maths Skills Booklet*.

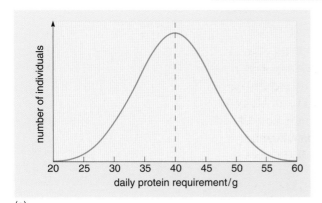

(a)

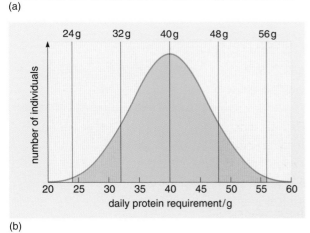

(b)

Figure SP3.1 (a) Sketch graph to show the daily protein requirement (in grams) of individuals in a hypothetical population. (b) Same graph to show the numbers of individuals falling within particular ranges of protein intake.

The physiological requirement of individuals for a particular nutrient varies. Most people will need an average amount, some people will need less than average, and some will need more (see Question SP3.3). If it were possible to measure the requirement of, say, protein, for every individual in a particular population, and all these measurements were plotted on a graph, then a curve shaped like that in Figure SP3.1 would be obtained. This is called a 'normal distribution curve'.

Figure SP3.1a shows that the mean (or average) protein requirement (the peak of the curve) is about 40 g per day, with most people needing somewhere near to that value and relatively few needing a great deal more or a great deal less. In order to be able to quantify the numbers of people who have unusual requirements, statisticians use a mathematical formula to calculate a value that they call the 'standard deviation'. Let's assume that this was done for the data in Figure SP3.1a and the calculated value for the standard deviation was 8 g. (Note that these data are hypothetical and these values have just been chosen to make the maths simple.) Values that are between 8 g above and 8 g below the mean value of 40 g, i.e. between 32 g and 48 g, are said to be within 'one standard deviation' of the mean. If you draw lines at these values from the horizontal axis upwards to meet the curve, as shown in Figure SP3.1b then the brown area under the curve represents 68% of all the measurements taken. (Remember that % means 'in every 100', so 68% of all the measurements means '68 in every 100 measurements'.) So, in this example, the protein requirement for 68% of the population would be between 32 g per day and 48 g per day.

● The required protein intake of 95% of the population lies within 2 standard deviations of the mean. What daily protein intake would this represent?

◐ 2 standard deviations would be 16 g, so the values would be calculated by 40 g – 16 g = 24 g, and by 40 g + 16 g = 56 g. Thus 95% of the population would require between 24 g and 56 g of protein per day (that is, the brown and purple areas in Figure SP3.1b). Only 5% of the population (5 people in every 100), would have requirements outside these limits (the two small red areas in the figure). Half of those (2.5%) would need less than 24 g and half would need more than 56 g of protein per day.

You should now look carefully at HN Figure 3.2 p. 42. This is a generalised graph for nutrient requirements and therefore does not have any specific values given on the horizontal axis. Measurements from large numbers of individuals have been used and the percentage of people with a particular nutrient requirement is plotted on the vertical axis. The peak value is labelled as the EAR, estimated average requirement. The EAR is indicated by the letter B and the levels that are two standard deviations either side of this (labelled as Mean + 2 SD and Mean − 2 SD) are labelled C and D.

With that background, now read HN p. 42 starting at 'Distribution of nutritional requirements in a population', to the start of 'Fats and carbohydrates' on p. 43.

As explained in HN p. 43, when the dietary reference value (DRV) tables were published in 1991, it was intended that these values, in particular the reference nutrient intake values (RNI), would replace the previously used recommended daily amounts (RDA). However, the European Union (EU) has continued to use RDA for many nutrients, and RNI values have been slow to gain acceptance. On most UK food labels you will still find the RDA values given for vitamins and minerals. References in HN to values from the DRV tables usually imply the RNI values.

Question SP3.4   (a) What is the name of the nutrient intake value that would provide sufficient of that nutrient for half of the population, but insufficient for the other half?

(b) Why is this value used for energy intake but not for the intake of vitamins and other nutrients?

(c) Why is this value only suitable for assessing the diet of groups of people and not for the diet of individuals? ◀

Some food manufacturers now include guideline daily amounts (GDA) on their labelling, as well as recommended daily amounts (RDA). The latter are given only for vitamins and minerals whereas GDA are broader and include more categories, such as energy (calories), fat, saturated fat, salt, total sugars, fibre, calcium and iron.

In this section, you have met several sets of initials (acronyms) that have rather similar meanings. This variety of names and initials causes considerable confusion for all those involved with nutrition, so if you are having difficulty sorting them all out, then please be reassured that you are not alone. You will probably find it very useful to make a list of these acronyms for yourself, with their meanings, so that you can refer to them as you continue with your study. The important ones so far are DRV, RNI, RDA, EAR and GDA. As you come across others, you can add them to your list.

Now read HN starting at 'Fats and carbohydrates' on p. 43. as far as the start of 'Dietary planning' on p. 46 and including the box containing HN Figure 3.3. HN Table 3.1 contains some types of nutrient that you have not yet met, but you will become familiar with most of them later in the course.

Question SP3.5   (a) What is the name of the nutrient intake value used by UK food manufacturers (e.g. those making breakfast cereals) for indicating the daily intake of vitamins?

(b) A new name has been chosen to replace that term, which was thought to be too prescriptive. What is the new name and its acronym?

(c) What percentage of the population would have insufficient of a particular vitamin if they consumed the RNI for that vitamin? ◀

3.6 Dietary planning

Read HN from 'Dietary planning' on p. 46 to the top of p. 52. Stop before the section entitled 'The question of alcohol'.

Question SP3.6 Write a description of the Balance of Good Health picture (Figure SP3.2) for a friend, who has not seen it, explaining what it shows and how its use can help towards a healthy diet. You should be able to do this task in about 200 words. ◀

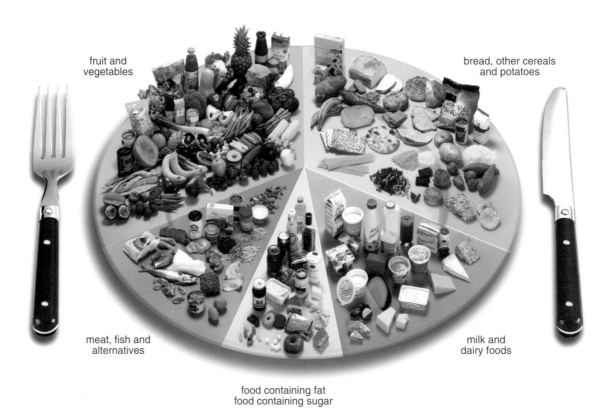

Figure SP3.2 The UK Balance of Good Health 2003 (an updated version of HN Figure 3.5).

● Compare HN Figure 3.5 on p. 48 with Figure SP3.2. What has remained the same and what changes, apart from presenting the new diagram in colour, have been made?

◉ The segments of the plate have remained the same size, so the relative proportions of the various sorts of foods needed to create a balanced diet, have not been changed. However, a much greater variety of foods have been illustrated in each segment, allowing more people to compare their own diet with the items on the plate.

If you are not familiar with fractions and percentages (%), you should now read the relevant section in the *Maths Skills Booklet*.

Activity SP3.1

This activity asks you to compare the example day's food intake shown in HN Figure 3.6 p. 50 and your own food intake for one day, with the recommended percentage of each food type advised by the UK Food Standards Agency.

Draw up a table with four columns and six rows. In the top row, put the following column headings: 'Food groups', 'Recommended % of food type', '% of that group in HN example diet' and '% of that group in my diet'. In the 'Food groups' column, copy down the list of foods given in the box on HN p. 48, and write the percentages next to them in the 'Recommended % of food type' column.

Now look at the way that the food groups have been identified in the right-hand column of the Today's menu example, in HN Figure 3.6, and then how the totals have been obtained for each food group. Use those totals to calculate the percentage of each food type in that diet. For example, there were six portions of bread/cereal in a total of 20 portions of food that day, so the calculation would be:

$$\frac{6}{20} \times 100\% = 30\%$$

Complete the calculations for the remaining food groups and enter them into your table. Draw an upward pointing arrow beside those food values that would need to be increased in the example diet, to meet the recommended dietary percentage, and a downward arrow beside those that should be decreased. Check your table so far with the one in the answer to this activity.

Now calculate the percentage of each food group in your own diet in the same way. You will need the list of your food intake for one day, as indicated at the start of this study period. Round your percentages to the nearest whole number and enter them at the appropriate place in the fourth column. You can check that you have done the calculations of percentages correctly, since they should add up to something very close to 100%. You will notice that the 'Recommended % of food type' column adds up to 101%, due to the small error introduced by rounding to the nearest whole number. Put an upward pointing arrow beside the food groups that you need to increase in your diet to meet the UK recommendations and a downward arrow beside those that you need to decrease.

Are there any surprises? Do you plan to make any changes to your diet on the basis of this exercise? You should keep your completed table safe as you may be asked to use it in a question in the course assessment. If you have the time and opportunity, you might like to record the diet of a friend or member of your family and add another column to your table.

3.7 Alcohol consumption

Now complete your study of HN Chapter 3 by reading 'The question of alcohol' pp. 52–53. Note that volumes are given in mL, which is an abbreviation for millilitres. There are 1000 millilitres in 1 litre. Elsewhere you may see litres abbreviated to 'l' and thus millilitres written as ml. If you are not familiar with the metric units of measurement, you should read the appropriate section in the *Maths Skills Booklet*.

You will have noticed the reference to a J-shaped relationship between overall mortality and alcohol consumption. Such a graph is shown in Figure SP3.3.

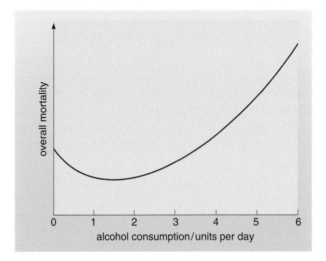

Figure SP3.3 The relationship between overall mortality and alcohol consumption.

● Describe in a couple of sentences what this graph shows.

◑ People who consume no alcohol have a slightly higher mortality rate than those who drink small amounts (1–2 units per day), while the mortality rate increases steadily in people who drink more than this.

Activity SP3.2

You might find it useful now to look through the articles and leaflets on nutrition and health that you have collected so far. Does your study of the course enable you to understand their content any better? You may know enough now to find inaccuracies in the material or general statements that do not apply to everyone in the population. Add to your folder any new examples of relevant material that you come across as you study the next part of the course.

Summary of SP3

1 Selecting a healthy diet involves choosing the appropriate foods in the quantities appropriate to age, habits, etc., and various guidelines for a healthy diet have been published.

2 Dietary reference values (DRVs) provide information on nutrient intakes, with the reference nutrient intake (RNI) being the amount that would be adequate for most of the population.

3 UK food labels still mostly use the older terminology of recommended daily amount (RDA) for vitamins and minerals.

4 Food guides published in the UK and the USA allow individuals to choose which foods to eat in which quantities to form a balanced diet.

5 Small amounts of alcohol can be beneficial to health.

This completes your study of the first part of HN. For the next seven study periods, you will be using this Study Book alone.

Answer to Activity SP3.1

Here is the partially completed table, before you have completed the final column with your own values.

Table SP3.1 Recommended percentages of various food groups in a balanced diet, and in two sample diets.

Food groups	Recommended % of food group	% of that group in HN example diet	% of that group in my diet
bread/cereals/potatoes	33	30 ↑	
fruit/vegetables	33	20 ↑	
meat/fish, etc.	12	20 ↓	
milk/dairy	15	10 ↑	
fat/sugar	8	20 ↓	

STUDY
PERIOD **4**

Proteins

The next three study periods will cover the macronutrients, protein, fat and carbohydrate. To understand their composition, digestion, function in the body, etc., you will need to have some knowledge of chemistry. If you already have some chemistry background, you will be able to work quite quickly through the first two sections of this study period.

As you read on, you will find that the word 'mass' is used, when you might expect to read 'weight'. Scientifically speaking, the amount of matter in an object is called its mass, while the word 'weight' is used to describe the downward pull on the same object due to gravity. If you were to go to the Moon, your mass, measured in kilograms, would remain the same, but your weight would be much less because the force of gravity is only about one-sixth as strong on the Moon as on the Earth. There is more information on mass and weight in the *Maths Skills Booklet*.

4.1 Atoms and molecules

Everything around us, and in us, is made up of atoms, which you can consider as minute spheres. They are very, very small. A page of this book is about one million (1 000 000) atoms thick. There are about 100 or so different types of atom, including oxygen atoms, carbon atoms, nitrogen atoms, gold atoms and iron atoms, and atoms provide the basic building blocks for everything. It is like having a 'Lego' set with about a hundred different types of brick. Each type of atom is a different size and has a different mass from all the other types. Because atoms are so very small, chemists do not deal with their actual mass, but instead they give the smallest and lightest atom, which is hydrogen, a mass of 1 and then express the mass of all the other atoms relative to that. So, for example, an oxygen atom is 16 times as heavy as a hydrogen atom and so it has a relative atomic mass of 16. The different types of atoms are called chemical elements or just elements, for short. By using different atoms, and joining them in different ways, you can produce water, sugar, salt, proteins, paper, rocks and, in fact, everything in the Universe! Different materials can exist as either a solid, a liquid or a gas, but one of these 'states' is most familiar. For example, water is generally thought of as a liquid, but it can freeze to a solid, ice, and it can occur as a gas, water vapour or steam.

● Air is not a pure gas, but a mixture of various different gases. Spend a few moments thinking of as many gases as you can, either occurring in the air or elsewhere.

● The following may be amongst the ones you have listed: oxygen, nitrogen, carbon dioxide, helium (familiar for its use to fill balloons, but also has many industrial uses), neon (in coloured signs), methane (the main component of natural gas), chlorine and hydrogen.

Helium and neon both exist as individual atoms in the atmosphere. But the smallest gaseous particle of hydrogen, oxygen, chlorine and nitrogen is composed of two identical atoms of the element attached together to form a molecule. The link between atoms, usually referred to as a chemical bond, can be represented by drawing a 'stick' holding the two 'balls', representing the atoms, together (Figure SP4.1).

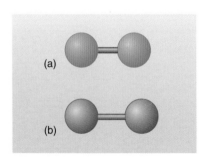

Figure SP4.1 Two of the elemental gases in the air, represented as ball-and-stick models. Molecules of (a) nitrogen (shown in blue) and (b) oxygen (shown in red) exist as pairs of atoms.

● The relative atomic mass of nitrogen is 14, so are nitrogen atoms heavier or lighter than oxygen atoms?

◑ As given above, an oxygen atom is 16 times heavier than a hydrogen atom. Oxygen has a relative atomic mass of 16. So oxygen atoms are slightly heavier than nitrogen atoms, whose relative atomic mass is 14 (each one is 14 times heavier than a hydrogen atom).

4.2 Chemical compounds

Many molecules consist of atoms of more than one type of element, and they are called compounds. Carbon dioxide, methane and water from the list of gases above are all chemical compounds. Water is the most abundant compound in living matter, and indeed on Earth, accounting for an average of 60% of total human body mass. A molecule of water, whether it exists as a gas in the atmosphere, as liquid water in our bodies or in lakes, rivers or seas, or as a solid in the form of ice, always has the same structure. It is a compound of two of the elements we have already met as gases, hydrogen and oxygen. A water molecule consists of two atoms of hydrogen and one atom of oxygen and can again be represented by a ball-and-stick model (Figure SP4.2a).

Carbon dioxide (Figure SP4.2b) consists of one carbon atom and two oxygen atoms.

● Look at the structure of a methane molecule in Figure SP4.2c. Which atoms does it contain? Is methane a compound?

◑ The atoms in methane are carbon and hydrogen – one carbon atom and four hydrogen atoms. Since the molecule is made up of two different elements, methane is a compound.

You will notice that the molecules of water, carbon dioxide and methane are different shapes. The water molecule has a 'bend' in it (all water molecules are exactly the same with a 'bend' of exactly the same angle). The atoms forming the carbon dioxide molecule are arranged in a straight line and the methane molecule is in the form of a triangular pyramid, called a tetrahedron, with hydrogen atoms at the corners and the carbon atom in the middle. Different molecules have different shapes and these shapes often play a crucial role in the behaviour ('properties') of the molecules in the human body and in other living things.

To make things quicker to draw when we are dealing with larger molecules, the atoms are not usually represented as coloured balls but by the chemical symbol for the element, and the bonds between the atoms are drawn as lines. Chemical analysis of the human body shows that 13 major elements, with small contributions from about 13 more, are present in a huge variety of different molecules. These elements and their chemical symbols are listed in Table SP4.1.

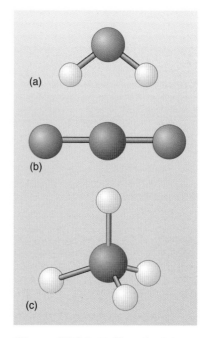

(a)

(b)

(c)

Figure SP4.2 Ball-and-stick representations of three small molecules. (a) A water molecule; oxygen and hydrogen atoms are represented by red and white balls, respectively. (b) A carbon dioxide molecule; carbon and oxygen atoms are represented by dark grey and red balls, respectively. (c) A methane molecule, using the same colour code.

Tables are used to provide information in a form which is easier to understand than if the same information were presented in normal text. As with diagrams, the first thing to read is the caption, which tells you what the table is about. Then look at the headings in the table, across the top of the columns or at the start of the rows, or sometimes both. In Table SP4.1, the headings – 'Element', 'Symbol' and 'Percentage of total body mass' – are across the top of the columns. So then you should glance down each column to see what it shows. The first column here is a list of names of chemical elements, but not, as you might expect, in alphabetical order. That should alert you to look elsewhere for the reason why that particular order has been chosen. The second column is the chemical symbol for each of the elements in the first column, in the same order. The third column is the percentage of the body mass that is made up of each of the elements and now the reason for the order of the elements becomes clear. As you glance down the 'Percentage of total body mass' column, you see that the numbers are in decreasing order, with oxygen being the element that makes up the greatest percentage of the body mass. Including 'percentage' in the column heading avoids the need for writing the symbol '%' beside every numerical value. Scanning down that column gives you more information about the relative quantities of the various elements in the body. Often it is more important to be aware of the general trends shown in a table of figures, rather than the exact values. In this case you might notice that oxygen, carbon and hydrogen together make up a very high percentage (actually 93%) of the body mass. The remaining small percentage (7%) is made up of small amounts of the other elements. You will have further opportunities to develop the skills of reading tables as you progress through the course.

Table SP4.1 The major elements by mass found in the human body (and most other mammals).

Element	Symbol	Percentage of total body mass
oxygen	O	65.0
carbon	C	18.5
hydrogen	H	9.5
nitrogen	N	3.2
calcium	Ca	1.5
phosphorus	P	1.0
potassium	K	0.4
sulfur	S	0.3
sodium	Na	0.2
chlorine	Cl	0.1
magnesium	Mg	0.1
iodine	I	0.1
iron	Fe	0.1

If you check the chemical symbols in Table SP4.1, you will find that many of them are the single initial letter of the element's name.

● In Table SP4.1, identify the chemical symbols for oxygen, carbon and hydrogen.

◉ The symbols are the single capital letters O, C and H, respectively.

Sometimes two letters are used, in which case the second one is written as a lower case (small) letter.

● What are the symbols for the following elements: calcium, chlorine, iodine, iron, magnesium, phosphorus, potassium and sodium?

◉ Calcium, Ca; chlorine, Cl; iodine, I; iron, Fe; magnesium, Mg; phosphorus, P; potassium, K; sodium, Na.

Some of these are obviously the first letter or two letters of the name of the element, as in Ca for calcium, or an obvious pair of letters, such as Mg for magnesium. Others are not so easy to work out. The symbol for sodium (Na) comes from the Arabic word *natron*, which is a salt lake in Egypt. The symbol for iron (Fe) comes from the Latin word *ferrum* which means iron or any implement made of iron.

● Draw the structure of a molecule of water (Figure SP4.2a) replacing the balls by letters and omitting the bend in the molecule.

◉ The structure of a water molecule is H−O−H; this is called its structural formula.

A water molecule can also be written by adding together the atoms to give H_2O, which is called the molecular formula.

● What is the disadvantage of writing the water molecule as H_2O?

◉ The molecular formula does not show the way in which the atoms are joined together, whereas the structural formula H−O−H shows that the oxygen atom is in between the two hydrogen atoms. The order in which the atoms are attached together in molecules is important and so you often find molecules drawn in the extended form.

● Look back at the structure of a methane molecule in Figure SP 4.2c. Re-draw the molecule using the symbols for the atoms instead of balls, drawing it flat on the page, rather than as a three-dimensional representation. Then add the atoms together and write the molecular formula.

◉ The structural formula of methane is usually represented as shown here. Its molecular formula is CH_4 which indicates one carbon atom and four hydrogen atoms but does not show clearly how they are linked.

$$H-\underset{\underset{H}{|}}{\overset{\overset{H}{|}}{C}}-H$$

In most of the molecules that you will meet, each type of atom has a fixed number of bonds to other atoms.

● Look back at the structural formulae of water and methane. How many bonds can each type of atom form?

◉ Hydrogen atoms (H) can only ever form one bond; oxygen atoms (O) can form two bonds and carbon atoms (C) can form four bonds. These numbers are important and worth remembering as carbon, hydrogen and oxygen are the most important atoms in living things. If you remember H_2O and CH_4, you will always be able to work out the number of bonds that each atom (H, O and C) can form.

Some people find it easier to think of the number of bonds as the number of 'arms' (or 'hooks') that an atom has. So, hydrogen has one 'arm' and can therefore 'hold hands' with only one other atom.

● The molecular formula for carbon dioxide is CO_2. Try to draw its structural formula giving the carbon and oxygen atoms the correct number of bonds.

◐ You may have found this quite difficult. Carbon has four 'arms' and each oxygen has two 'arms'. So, if each oxygen 'holds hands' with two of carbon's 'hands', then the formula would be as shown here. When there are two lines joining two atoms, then the bond is known as a double bond. So in this case we have a double bond between each of the oxygen atoms and the carbon atom.

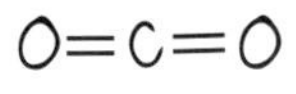

$$O = C = O$$

Carbon is a very unusual element as carbon atoms can bond with each other to form long chains, joined usually by single bonds, and sometimes by double bonds.

● Draw a line of six carbon atoms, joined to each other by single bonds. Remember to give each carbon atom the correct number of bonds ('arms') even though some of them will have nothing to bond to.

◐

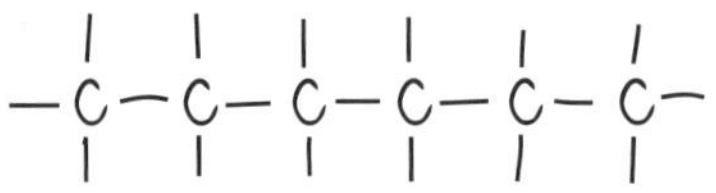

This structure, of course, does not represent a complete molecule; but if a hydrogen atom is present on each of the bonds, then it is the compound hexane, which is a relative of the gas methane and behaves in similar ways. Its molecular formula would be C_6H_{14}.

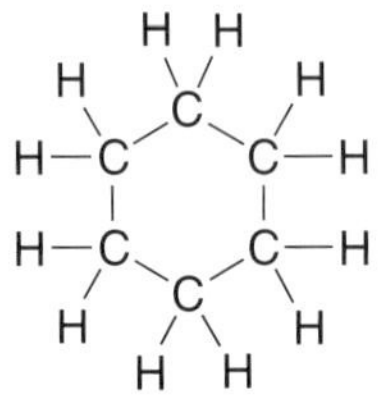

Carbon atoms can also join together to form rings. Cyclohexane has its six carbon atoms arranged in a circle, as shown here.

● How many fewer hydrogen atoms are there in cyclohexane, compared with the straight-chain hexane above?

◐ There are two less (14 in straight-chain hexane and only 12 in cyclohexane), because the end two carbon atoms of straight-chain hexane are bonded to one another in cyclohexane, reducing the number of 'arms' available to bond to hydrogen.

● A compound called benzene is another example of a molecule composed of a ring of six carbon atoms, but this molecule has alternate double and single bonds between them. Draw a benzene molecule, remembering to ensure that each carbon atom has four bonds and to attach hydrogen atoms to all the spare bonds. Write down the molecular formula of benzene.

● See opposite – there are six carbon atoms and six hydrogen atoms, so the molecular formula of benzene is C_6H_6. This structure is often drawn just showing the ring shape and the double bonds, omitting the carbon and hydrogen atoms (as you will see shortly).

Carbon is the basis of all the molecules that make up the macronutrients in our diet. Since the molecules consist of large numbers of carbon atoms, they can also be called macromolecules. So, with this chemical background, we will now move on to look at the detailed structure of the first of the macronutrients in our diet, protein.

4.3 The importance of protein

● From general knowledge about foods, what would you say are the main sources of protein in the average person's diet in the UK?

● Most people think of meat, fish, eggs and cheese as the main protein sources, though someone on a strictly vegetarian diet would list quite different sources, such as nuts and pulses (peas and beans).

Protein occurs in a wide range of foods as shown in Table SP4.2.

You will notice that the column headings in Table SP4.2 which indicate the amount of protein in the various foods are written as 'Protein content/%'. You can read this as 'Protein content expressed as %'. This is the scientifically correct way to show the units of the values given in a table. The same method is also used for labelling the axes of graphs. So the value shown has been divided by the unit in which it is measured.

Table SP4.2 The protein content (as % by mass) of some common foods.

Animal-derived foods	Protein content/%	Plant-derived foods	Protein content/%
cheese (Cheddar)	26	soya flour (low fat)	45
chicken (no skin)	25	soya flour (full fat)	37
bacon (lean)	20	peanuts	24
beef (lean)	20	bread (wholemeal)	9
cod	17	bread (white)	8
herring	17	rice	7
eggs	12	peas (fresh)	6
milk	3	potatoes (old)	2
cheese (cream)	3	bananas	1
butter	less than 1	apples	less than 1

● Eggs are usually considered to be a high-protein food and yet they contain only 12% protein. Can you suggest any reason why this value is apparently so low? Think about the physical composition of the inside of an egg, compared with that of the high protein foods listed in the table.

● None of the high-protein foods listed contain very much water. In their normal condition, all of them are dry solids. Yet fresh eggs contain a great deal of water, which is why the inside of an egg is rather runny. Dried egg contains a much higher percentage of protein. You might think that a hard-boiled egg, which is fairly solid, is also dry. Does it contain less water? No, it does not; the water is still present, but trapped amongst the protein molecules. You will discover more about eggs later. The protein contents of meat and fish are similarly lower than those of flour, cheese and peanuts, due to the inclusion of significant amounts of water in them.

Although Table SP4.2 and the nutritional information on food packaging lists 'protein' as though it were a single substance, there are tens of thousands of different proteins in living organisms. Life is based on proteins and the word 'protein' itself is derived from a Greek word meaning 'holding first place'. Proteins form an integral part of the components of all living cells and a typical cell in the human body contains 18% protein, though some cell types, such as muscle cells, contain much more. In fact, most of the food that we call 'meat' is actually muscle. Some proteins have a largely structural role in the body, forming tendons and hair, others are produced in and then released from cells (secreted) and function as enzymes and hormones. The proteins we eat are digested by enzymes, which are themselves proteins. Some types of protein form part of the immune system, which protects us against infection, while others play a vital part in blood clotting. However, they all have the same fundamental structure. They are built of small molecules called amino acids. Large molecules composed of small subunits are called polymers, and the subunits, in this case the amino acids, are monomers. So protein polymers are made up of amino acid monomers.

4.4 The chemistry of amino acids

Human proteins are composed of 20 different amino acids (Table SP4.3).

● Look through the names of the amino acids. With a few exceptions, what common feature do you notice in the names?

● Nearly all of them end in the three letters '-ine'. You may find this suffix a useful way to recognise an amino acid name in this course, although lots of other biological molecules end in '-ine' and are not amino acids.

Eight of the 20 are the so-called essential amino acids; that is, they cannot be made in the human body and so have to be present in the diet. There are two others (tyrosine and cysteine) that can only be synthesised from essential amino acids and a further one (histidine) that is made in only small amounts and so should be included in the diet. The amino acid arginine is essential only for young children.

Table SP4.3 Essential and non-essential amino acids (with their 3-letter abbreviations).

Essential amino acids	Amino acids synthesised from essential amino acids	Non-essential amino acids
lysine (Lys)	tyrosine (Tyr)*	glycine (Gly)
methionine (Met)	cysteine (Cys)†	alanine (Ala)
threonine (Thr)		serine (Ser)
leucine (Leu)		proline (Pro)
isoleucine (Ile)		glutamate (Glu)
valine (Val)		glutamine (Gln)
phenylalanine (Phe)		aspartate (Asp)
tryptophan (Try)		asparagine (Asn)
histidine (His) – made only in very small amounts in the body		
arginine (Arg) – for young children		

* Synthesised from phenylalanine.
† Synthesised from methionine.

● Suggest why arginine is not an essential amino acid in adults.

◐ The most likely reason is that older children and adults can synthesise arginine from other amino acids.

The many thousands of different proteins, each with a particular biological function, have an enormous variety of structures. How can this be if there are only 20 different amino acids? The answer is that when several hundred of the 20 different types link up to form a protein chain, there is a huge number of possible sequences. Each particular type of protein molecule has its own unique sequence of amino acids along its length. Some amino acids may not be used at all in a protein, while others may occur many times.

The basic structure of all amino acids is similar and is based around a carbon atom with different atoms, or groups of atoms, attached to each of its four bonds. Remember that the bonds of a carbon atom are actually arranged in a tetrahedral shape (see Figure SP4.2c) with the carbon atom at the centre, but we shall be drawing the molecules as though they were flat, for simplicity.

● Devise a simple table giving the names, chemical symbols and number of bonds expected for all the elements present in the simplest amino acid, glycine, whose structure is shown in Figure SP4.3a.

◐ Table SP4.4 is my version of the table, together with a suitable title. I could have listed the elements in a different order, such as alphabetically, but I chose to list them in order of decreasing number of bonds.

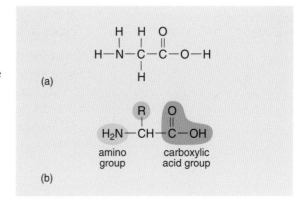

Figure SP4.3 (a) Structural formula of the simplest amino acid, glycine. (b) Structural formula of a generalised amino acid.

Table SP4.4 Elements found in the amino acid glycine, with their chemical symbols and number of bonds.

Name of element	Chemical symbol	Number of bonds
carbon	C	4
nitrogen	N	3
oxygen	O	2
hydrogen	H	1

You might like to check that all the atoms in glycine have the correct number of bonds. Two of the bonds from the central carbon are attached to hydrogen atoms, one pointing upwards and one pointing down. To the left, the carbon atom is attached to a nitrogen atom, which itself has two hydrogen atoms attached. This group of three atoms, which can be written as NH_2 (or the other way round as H_2N), is called an amino group. To the right, the central carbon atom is attached to another carbon atom, and that one is attached to one oxygen atom, pointing up, by a double bond, and via a single bond to another oxygen atom, which has a hydrogen atom bonded to it. That group of atoms, COOH, is called a carboxylic acid group (or sometimes just a carboxyl group). Conventionally, amino acids are drawn this way round, with the amino group to the left and the acid group to the right, as their name suggests.

● How many atoms in total, and how many of each element, are present in a molecule of glycine?

◑ There are 10 atoms in glycine; five hydrogen atoms, two each of carbon and oxygen, and one nitrogen atom.

● Now look at Figure SP4.3b which gives the formula of a generalised amino acid, and identify four differences between that and the representation of the glycine molecule in Figure SP4.3a.

◑ The differences are:

  • The upward pointing hydrogen atom H, on the central carbon C, has been replaced by R.

  • The downward pointing hydrogen atom H has been written beside the central carbon atom, as CH.

  • The two hydrogen atoms attached to the nitrogen atom N have been written beside it as H_2N. You will recall that this is the amino group, which can also be written as NH_2. Writing it here as H_2N shows more clearly that it is the N atom (and not one of the hydrogen atoms) that is bonded to the C atom.

  • The hydrogen atom H to the right has been written beside the oxygen O atom, as OH.

So the only real difference is the presence of the R. There is no element with the symbol R. This R is used to indicate that a number of different atoms or groups of atoms can be placed here – each amino acid has a different one. The smallest amino acid is glycine, where R is simply a hydrogen atom.

● How many different R groups would you expect to find in the amino acids named in Table SP4.3?

◐ There are 19 other amino acids, excluding glycine, so there will be 19 different groups, one for each of them.

The formulae of some of these R groups are given in Table SP4.5.

Table SP4.5 Seven amino acids found in proteins.

Name and pronunciation	Formula of R group
glycine ('gly-seen')	H—
phenylalanine ('fee-nile-alla-neen')	(benzene ring)—CH_2—
lysine ('lie-seen')	$\overset{+}{N}H_3$—$(CH_2)_4$—
alanine ('alla-neen')	CH_3—
aspartate ('ass-part-ate')	$O{=}C{-}O^-$ / CH_2—
serine ('seer-een')	OH—CH_2—
cysteine ('sis-tayn')	SH—CH_2—

● What structure do you recognise in the R group of phenylalanine?

◐ Phenylalanine has a ring that looks very much like benzene attached to a —CH_2— group. Look back to SP4.2 if you don't remember what the complete benzene molecule looks like. Note that in this representation, the C and H atoms are omitted.

4.5 Linking amino acids

4.5.1 Linking two amino acids

As we have seen earlier, atoms can combine to form molecules and now we will see how molecules can combine together to make bigger molecules. If two glycine molecules are placed side by side, as in Figure SP4.4a, we can see how it

Figure SP4.4 (a) Two molecules of glycine, side by side, showing how a water molecule can be formed using OH from one and H from the other. (b) The two glycine molecules are linked together to form a dipeptide.

is possible to remove one hydrogen and one oxygen atom from the left-hand one, and one hydrogen atom from the right-hand one, to make a water molecule, leaving a spare bond ('arm') to link the carbon (C) atom from the amino acid on the left with the N atom from the one on the right, as in Figure SP4.4b. This bond is called a peptide bond (or sometimes an amide bond) and the new molecule is called a dipeptide (the prefix di- means 'two'). The word 'peptide' comes from the Greek *peptos* meaning 'digested'. You might like to check that after this joining process, all the atoms involved still retain the correct number of bonds – 4 for carbon, 3 for nitrogen, 2 for oxygen and 1 for hydrogen.

4.5.2 Linking more amino acids

Consider what would be possible if you placed another glycine molecule to the right of the dipeptide shown in Figure SP4.4b. Another peptide bond could be formed between them to give a chain of three glycine molecules, a tripeptide (tri- means 'three' as in a word like tricycle). Adding another one would give a chain of four glycines, and so on. In fact, you could make a molecule of as many glycine molecules as you wanted. You might find it easier to think of them as railway trucks, with a hook on each end, being joined together to form a long train. Of course, all the amino acids have 'hooks' on each end of the molecule, so an almost infinite variety of proteins are possible, using the whole range of amino acids. In the train analogy, you could join all sorts of different trucks and carriages together to make a train, as long as they all had the same sort of hook on the end of them. In chemical terms, a chain of many amino acids joined together is called a polypeptide (poly- means 'many'). A long polypeptide chain, with various amino acids attached together in the correct order is called a protein, though some proteins are made up of more than one polypeptide chain. Biologists often use the words 'polypeptide' and 'protein' interchangeably.

● Can you recall from SP4.4, how many amino acids are linked together to form a typical protein molecule?

◍ Several hundred amino acids is typical. For example, the protein part of the haemoglobin molecule, which transports oxygen around the body (SP1.7) consists of four polypeptide chains, two made up from 141 amino acids and two from 146 amino acids.

4.5.3 Amino acid sequences

With 20 different amino acids as constituents and proteins several hundred amino acids long, it would in theory be possible to construct an almost infinite number of different protein molecules. But a particular protein only functions correctly in the body if it is made of a particular set of amino acids joined together in *precisely* the correct sequence.

● In what form does the code exist that enables cells to make proteins and all their other components? You may need to look back to SP1.6.

● The code exists in the DNA, which is present in chromosomes in the nuclei of human cells. This code gives the sequence of amino acids needed to make each protein.

The first protein whose amino acid sequence was worked out in the laboratory was insulin, a hormone secreted by the pancreas. Although insulin is composed of only 51 amino acids (as you will see later in Figure SP4.8), it nevertheless took almost six years for a group of research scientists in Cambridge to complete the task. The group was headed by Frederick Sanger, who was awarded the Nobel Prize for this work in 1958. Since then, the speed of finding out the sequence of amino acids in a protein (a process known as 'sequencing') has increased hugely and the time for the process can now be measured in hours, rather than years.

4.6 Protein shapes and functions

Although a protein may be composed simply of a single long chain of amino acids, it does not remain as an elongated string, but folds up into a very precise shape. The shape may be regular, like a helix (Figure SP4.5) or a zigzag sheet, or it may appear very irregular like a tangled piece of string (Figure SP4.6). The three-dimensional shape of most proteins consists of a mixture of these different arrangements. However, unlike a piece of string, each molecule of the protein is, in fact, folded into precisely the same shape and that shape is crucial to its correct functioning in the body.

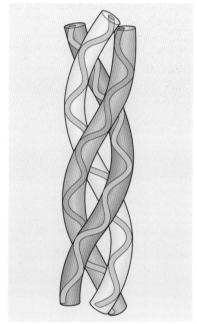

Figure SP4.5 Structure of collagen, an important component of skin, tendons, bone and many other tissues. A collagen molecule is a triple helix, composed of three polypeptide chains, which are themselves helical, coiled around each other.

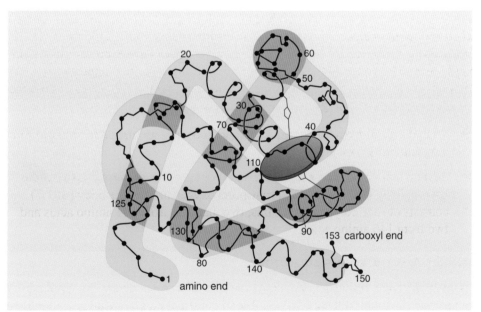

Figure SP4.6 Structure of myoglobin, a protein that binds to oxygen molecules in muscles. The black dots, some of which are numbered, are the amino acids and the red disc is the oxygen-binding group. The 'folded sausage' shows the overall shape of the protein. Note that numbering always goes from the amino ('left hand') end to the carboxyl ('right hand') end of a protein, and this reflects the order in which the amino acids are put together when the protein is made by a cell.

4.6.1 Determining the shape

During your studies you will meet a number of words which have Latin or Greek roots and whose meaning you may be able to work out. Coming up very soon are the words 'hydrophobic' and 'hydrophilic'. You probably recognise hydro- as being related to 'water' (it is from the Greek word for water), since it occurs in words like hydroelectric, hydrothermal, hydroponics, hydrostatic, etc. Even the element hydrogen was named because it was originally generated (*genos* in Greek means 'descent') from water. The second half of the words, -phobic and -philic, mean 'hating' and 'beloved', respectively, from the Greek words *phobos* which means 'fear' and *philos*, 'friend'. As you read on, you will meet disulfide – where di- means 'two' (from the Greek *dis* meaning twice) and -sulfide means related to the element sulfur. You have already met carbon dioxide (a gas made up of one carbon and two oxygen atoms) and dipeptide, two amino acid molecules joined together. Sometimes the Latin prefix bi- is used as an alternative for 'two' as in bicycle, binoculars, etc. Tri- means 'three' (the Latin and Greek roots are similar), as in tripod (*podos* is 'foot' in Greek), and poly- (as in polypeptide) means 'many' (*polys* is 'much' in Greek).

The way in which each particular protein molecule folds is determined by a range of different interactions between the amino acids that make it up. Four of the most important ones will be considered here.

Firstly, some of the side chains of the amino acids – the R groups – a few of which were listed in Table SP4.5 are hydrophobic, that is, they tend to associate with one another and to repel (or exclude) water molecules. The side chain of phenylalanine, containing the benzene ring, is one example. Since the inside of the body provides a watery (aqueous) environment, the protein chain folds up with these hydrophobic groups clustered together on the inside, and the hydrophilic groups on the outside, as shown in Figure SP4.7.

Figure SP4.7 How a protein folds with its hydrophobic amino acids interacting with each other on the inside, and its hydrophilic groups interacting with water, on the outside.

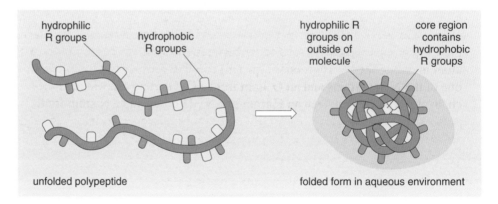

Secondly, some of the amino acid R groups carry a positive or negative electrical charge, written as + or – , on one of their atoms. Opposite charges (+ and –) attract one another, and similar charges repel each other. These attractions and repulsions, called ionic interactions since the charged molecules are called ions, play a part in determining the shape that the protein adopts.

● From Table SP4.5, identify two amino acids that will attract one another and two that will repel one another.

◔ The amino acid lysine has a positive charge, whereas aspartate has a negative charge. If these amino acids occur in a protein, they can attract one another and bend the protein chain so that they lie close together. On the other hand, two lysines, both with a positive charge, will repel one another, pushing the two parts of the protein chain apart where they occur. Similarly, two aspartates, each with a negative charge, will also repel one another.

The third type of interaction is called hydrogen bonding. Although hydrogen bonds are weaker than the bonds that hold the atoms together to make up the amino acids in the protein chain, hydrogen bonding nevertheless plays a very important role, not only in protein folding, but elsewhere in chemistry too, particularly in conferring on water its unique properties. Hydrogen bonding depends on *partial* positive and negative charges (much smaller than those mentioned above) which are present in some molecules. A hydrogen bond can occur between a hydrogen atom with a partial positive charge (by virtue of its attachment to an oxygen or a nitrogen atom) in one part of the molecule, and a different oxygen atom or nitrogen atom (which has a partial negative charge), elsewhere in the same molecule, or in another molecule. A hydrogen bond is normally represented by a dashed (or dotted) line, as follows:

(i) $-O-H\text{------}O-$

(ii) $-O-H\text{------}N-$

(iii) $-N-H\text{------}O-$

(iv) $-N-H\text{------}N-$

● Look back at Figure SP4.4b and identify which of the hydrogen bonding types (i)–(iv) could occur in proteins.

◔ All of these are possible. Figure SP4.4b shows only two amino acids joined together, but a complete polypeptide molecule would contain C=O and N—H groups at regular intervals along the chain. So, type (i) could occur between an O—H group at the end of each protein chain, or an O—H group in the R group of an amino acid such as serine (see Table SP4.5), and an O atom in any one of the C=O groups. Type (ii) could occur between the same O—H groups and a N atom in one of the N—H groups. Type (iii) could occur between the H from one of the N—H groups and an O atom from a C=O group elsewhere in the chain and type (iv) between an H from one N—H group and a N atom from another N—H group elsewhere. There will also be hydrogen bonding between some of the R groups of the amino acids making up the protein chain.

These hydrogen bonds hold parts of the protein together and they constitute another of the reasons the molecule adopts a particular shape.

Finally, the shape of a protein molecule can be stabilised by disulfide bridges which are standard bonds that form between two sulfur atoms in the R groups of the amino acid, cysteine (see Table SP4.5). This type of bond can occur both between two cysteines in the same polypeptide chain (intra-chain bridge) and between cysteines in adjacent polypeptide chains (inter-chain bridge), holding together two polypeptide chains to form a single protein molecule. You can see both intra- and inter-chain disulfide bridges in the hormone insulin in Figure SP4.8.

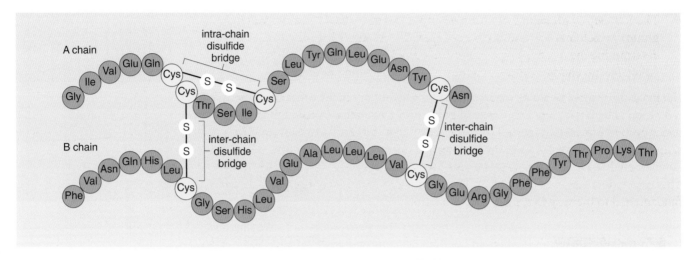

Figure SP4.8 Simplified structure of insulin, a protein containing disulfide bridges.

● Reading from the left-hand end, list the names of the first seven amino acids in the B chain of the insulin molecule in Figure SP4.8. You will need to use Table SP4.3.

● The amino acids are: phenylalanine (Phe), valine (Val), asparagine (Asn), glutamine (Gln), histidine (His), leucine (Leu) and cysteine (Cys).

Question SP4.1 (a) List the four interactions described above that determine the shape of a protein molecule, and briefly summarise the features of each one.

(b) Occasionally, due to a change (mutation) in the DNA code for a particular protein, a protein is synthesised with an incorrect amino acid at one position along the chain. Taking each of the four interactions in turn, consider whether a change in that single amino acid is likely to alter the shape and therefore disrupt the function of the protein in the body. ◀

4.6.2 A faulty shape

An example of the effect of a single change in the amino acid sequence of a protein is provided by haemoglobin, the protein in the red blood cells that binds oxygen as it is transported from the lungs to the cells elsewhere in the body. The sixth amino acid in the haemoglobin chain starting from the amino end, is normally glutamate, but in some individuals, valine appears there instead, profoundly altering the shape of the haemoglobin molecule.

● The R groups of glutamate and valine are shown below.

$$
\begin{array}{cc}
\text{COO}^- & \text{H}_3\text{C} \quad \text{CH}_3 \\
| & \diagdown \diagup \\
\text{CH}_2 & \text{CH} \\
| & | \\
\text{CH}_2 & \\
| & \text{valine} \\
\text{glutamate} &
\end{array}
$$

Why do you think the shape of the haemoglobin molecule is affected so much when valine replaces glutamate?

● The R group of glutamate carries a negative charge ($-COO^-$, carboxylate group), which interacts with other charged groups and is important in determining the overall shape of the haemoglobin molecule. The R group of valine has no charge and so is unable to take part in such interactions.

Haemoglobin molecules with valine at position 6 fold up into the wrong shape. The red blood cells containing this type of haemoglobin assume a curved 'sickle' shape under certain conditions, as shown in Figure SP4.9a, instead of the normal disc shape (see Figure SP1.3). This altered shape is distinctive of the condition known as 'sickle cell disease'. The characteristics of the disease are shown in Figure SP4.9b. This case is just one example of how the correct amino acid sequence of a protein is fundamental to the way that the protein functions.

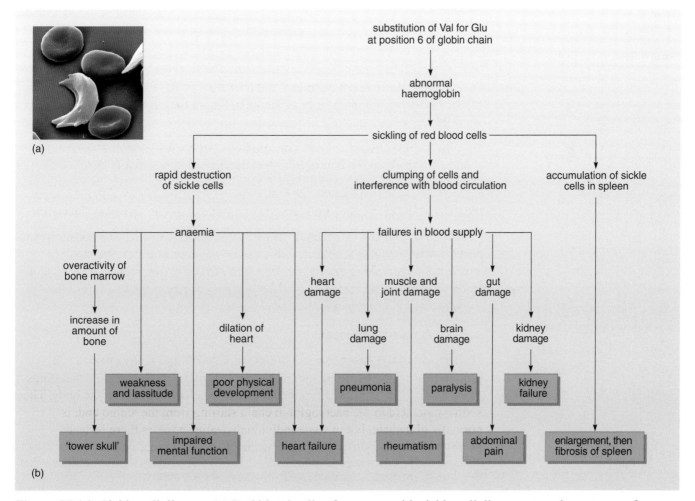

Figure SP4.9 Sickle cell disease. (a) Red blood cells of a person with sickle cell disease, at various stages of sickling. (b) Origin and characteristics of sickle cell disease.

4.6.3 Cooking eggs

Many solids melt as they get hotter, but eggs do not. They start as quite liquid in the fresh state and when they are heated, they go solid. This behaviour is a result of the effect of the heat on the proteins they contain. The proteins of both the egg yolk and white are folded into precise shapes (SP4.6.1), each molecule forming a minute ball called a globular protein. But when these proteins are heated, some of the interactions holding the protein molecules into their precise globular shapes are broken and the molecules begin to unravel. This enables the separate protein chains to become entangled with one another and new interactions can form, particularly hydrogen bonds and the stronger disulfide bridges, which create a solid three-dimensional network of protein molecules, leading to a soft-boiled or eventually a hard-boiled egg.

● Which amino acid forms disulfide bridges and which element does it contain?

◉ Disulfide bridges form between the R side-chains of the amino acid cysteine, which contains sulfur (Figure SP4.8).

When an egg begins to go 'bad', its proteins break down and the sulfur from the cysteines forms a gas called hydrogen sulfide (H_2S), which has the characteristic and very unpleasant smell of 'rotten eggs'.

Coagulation (solidification) of proteins can be caused by acidity, as well as by heat. Some people add vinegar or lemon juice to the water in which they are boiling eggs. If the eggshell cracks, and the white of the egg (albumen) begins to escape, the protein in it coagulates more quickly in the slightly acidic water than it would do in 'plain' (neutral) water, sealing the crack.

Whisking egg whites also causes the globular proteins to unravel and take up new shapes, but this time air is trapped in the three-dimensional network that they form. Baking the whisked egg white causes coagulation, and the protein becomes solid, forming a meringue. If fat molecules are present, they coat the globular proteins and prevent them from unravelling and tangling when they are whisked, which is why you cannot make a meringue if any of the egg yolk, which contains fat, is present in the egg white.

4.7 Protein digestion and absorption

The process of digestion is defined in the *Glossary* as the 'process by which macromolecules in food are broken down into their component small-molecule subunits'.

● In the case of proteins, what are the 'macromolecules' and what are the 'small-molecule subunits'? What type of bond has to be broken to separate the subunits?

◉ The macromolecules are, of course, the proteins or polypeptides themselves, and the subunits are the amino acids. The bonds holding the subunits together are peptide bonds (see SP4.5.1).

This breakdown would happen impossibly slowly without the involvement of digestive enzymes, which are themselves proteins. Enzymes are often named by adding the ending '-ase' to the name of the substance on which they work. So, the enzymes that break down peptide bonds are called peptidases (protein-digesting enzymes). Although all amino acids are joined by the same peptide bond, the type of R group on the amino acids on either side of the bond affects the action of the peptidases so much that several different enzymes are usually needed to digest a protein molecule completely.

Protein digestion starts in the stomach, the walls of which secrete hydrochloric acid.

● What effect would you expect hydrochloric acid to have on proteins? (Hint: recall the effect of adding vinegar to the water in which eggs are being boiled.)

○ Acids cause proteins to coagulate, by affecting the bonds holding globular proteins into their normal shape.

An enzyme, called pepsin, produced by cells lining the wall of the stomach, starts to attack some of the peptide bonds and splits the long protein chains into shorter polypeptides. Then more peptidases are released from the pancreas into the small intestine, where they split the polypeptide chains into even smaller lengths and begin to remove individual amino acids from the ends of the chains. Digestion of virtually all the protein in the food into individual amino acids is completed by more peptidases released directly from the cells lining the small intestine. The amino acids are then transported across the wall of the small intestine into the bloodstream. The blood carries them to all the cells of the body, where they can be absorbed and used by each type of cell to make its own particular types of protein by linking them together again, in the order determined by the DNA in the chromosomes.

Activity SP4.1

You should now try to summarise this information about protein digestion and absorption in the form of a diagram or flow chart, or a mix of both. The process of trying out various kinds of diagrams, and discovering which ways are more successful and which less so, is as valuable in terms of clarifying your understanding of the topic as the end-product will be. So, take a sheet of paper, and try to summarise the information on protein digestion in a diagrammatic way. Then compare your version, or versions, with those at the end of this study period. Make a note of how you think you could improve on your version if you were asked to do a similar exercise again.

Protein digestion is normally very efficient and virtually all of the protein (98%) that is eaten by an adult is fully digested to amino acids and absorbed. However, the digestive systems of newborn babies are somewhat less efficient, which has important functional implications. Mothers' milk contains antibodies, which are a type of protein important in providing immunity against infections. If the infant digestive system were as efficient as that of an adult, these antibodies would be digested like any other protein. However, a slightly less efficient digestive system allows the antibodies to remain intact and to pass from the gut into the bloodstream, so providing essential immunity for the new baby. However, other proteins, such as those in cows' milk could also pass through to the baby's bloodstream undigested and can be the source of some allergies or food intolerances later in life. Artificial (formula) milks for babies are designed to minimise this risk, but this is an important reason in favour of breastfeeding where possible.

4.7.1 Protein balance

The blood vessels that pass close to the digestive system and collect the amino acids absorbed from the small intestine, travel first to the liver. The liver appears to monitor the amounts of the different amino acids in the blood and it is in the liver that some amino acids can be converted chemically from one type to another, to fulfil the body's requirements for the synthesis of its own proteins. Normal human diets do not contain the exact mix of amino acids that the body needs, and so this interconversion is a vital part of the body's metabolism.

4.7.2 Too much protein

There is no way of storing large quantities of amino acids in the human body and so if more are present in the blood than are needed, the surplus ones have to be broken down and removed from the body. The liver carries out this crucially important function. The amino (nitrogen-containing) part of the amino acid is converted into a substance called urea, which contains the unwanted nitrogen. The urea is then carried round in the bloodstream to the kidneys where it is removed and then excreted from the body dissolved in water in the urine. All animals have to undertake a similar process to get rid of their excess amino acids, though the form of the nitrogen-containing waste product depends on how much water is available to dilute it. Fish produce ammonia, which is soluble and needs large amounts of water to remove it from the body, and can be toxic at high concentrations in the blood. Ammonia (in solution) is lost via their gills. Birds, which often do not have easy access to water, produce a semi-solid white sludge of uric acid. The remaining (carbon-containing) part of the amino acid can be broken down in humans and other animals, to provide energy or it can be stored by being converted to carbohydrate or fat, depending on the identity of the R group.

4.7.3 Too little protein

If insufficient protein is present in the diet for the body's needs, then it starts to break down its own proteins. Since muscles contain large amounts of protein, the result of a low-protein diet is muscle-wasting. Individuals who have a poor appetite, perhaps due to some underlying medical condition, may also be short of protein and muscle weakness is common. Muscle wasting is particularly hard to detect in obese patients where the reduction in size of the muscles is not easily detectable beneath the layer of fat.

In some parts of the world, many millions of people are short of protein in their diet, though they are probably short of other essential dietary components too, and it is not easy to identify the particular part that protein deficiency plays in their overall malnutrition. Protein-energy malnutrition (PEM) is a condition where the diet of adults and children is lacking in a range of nutrients and overall food intake is too low for their bodily requirements. Marasmus is a severe form of PEM, resulting from a long-term insufficiency in energy intake. It is a condition that is often seen in famines, although low-level marasmus can occur throughout a vulnerable population, with only the most severe cases being noticed. If no other source of energy is available, the protein in the body's muscles and organs is broken down to provide energy. The cells lining the digestive system are affected, leading to poor absorption of nutrients from the inadequate diet. This cycle of inadequate diet and poor absorption of nutrients leads to the severe body wasting seen in famine victims. Kwashiorkor is protein deficiency in children. It can occur when children are weaned from breast milk onto protein-poor foods such as cassava (a root vegetable) or plantain (green bananas). Repeated childhood infections and a lack of vitamins and minerals make the condition worse. The characteristic features are oedema, which is swelling of parts of the body due to fluid retention, and a general lack of energy for any activity. Growth stops and there is severe liver damage, loss of weight and loss of pigmentation from the skin.

4.7.4 Nitrogen balance

In a healthy person, there should be a balance between the input of nitrogen to the body and its output. The input is mostly from protein, though some other foods may contain small quantities of nitrogen too. The output of nitrogen is mainly in urine, with a little in the faeces from undigested protein, from cells shed from the gut lining and from bacteria that live in the colon. Nitrogen is also lost from the body in the proteins of skin cells which are continuously shed, and in hair and nails, which consist of the protein keratin. Studies indicate that if there is no protein in the diet, 0.34 g protein per kg of body mass is lost from the body each day.

● For a person with a body mass of 60 kg, how much protein would be needed in the diet each day to replace the amount lost?

◑ The amount of protein needed would be (0.34 × 60) g = 20.4 g.

However, for good health, more protein than this theoretical amount is needed. For example, for females aged between 19 and 50, the estimated average requirement, EAR, is 36.0 g per day, while the reference nutrient intake, RNI, is 45.0 g per day.

● Why is the EAR value lower than the RNI value for protein?

◑ The EAR is the average amount of protein required for the whole population, so half of the population (50%) would need more than this value (and half would need less). The RNI on the other hand, is the protein intake that would be sufficient for 97.5% of the population, so only 2.5% would need more than this. So inevitably the EAR value will be lower than the RNI value.

Extra dietary protein is needed by people who are suffering from injury, infection, burns and cancer, as all these conditions increase the rate of loss of protein from the body. The upper safe limit of protein intake is probably around 1.5 g per kg of body mass per day. Higher intakes may cause loss of minerals from the bones (which can result in more fractures), possibly due to the loss of more calcium in the urine, and may possibly contribute to a decline in kidney function, although this effect has yet to be confirmed.

Question SP4.2 The Expenditure and Food Survey (DEFRA 2001/2) gives a value of 71.3 g for the daily intake of protein in the UK. How much greater than the RNI is this value for a female aged 40, expressed (a) as an amount and (b) as a percentage of the RNI? ◀

Question SP4.3 (a) For a woman weighing 60 kg, what is the safe (maximum) limit of protein intake?

(b) How many times greater is this value than the EAR value?

(c) Use Table SP4.2 to calculate how much protein is present in a 250 g (about 8 oz) lean steak and thus whether eating this amount of meat on a daily basis would exceed the safe limit. ◀

Activity SP4.2

For women over 50, the EAR for protein is 37.2 g and the RNI is 46.5 g. For men over 50, the corresponding values are 42.6 g and 53.3 g. For men between 19 and 50, the values are 44.4 g and 55.5 g.

(a) Construct a table to present the values clearly for both genders and the two age ranges.

(b) Identify which values are appropriate to you, or another adult whom you know. Use the information from Table SP4.2, and perhaps information on the protein content from food labels, to estimate that person's daily protein intake and compare it to the values in your table.

Summary of SP4

1   The human body, and everything else, is made up of atoms.

2   There are about 26 different sorts of atom in the human body, combined into numerous different sorts of molecules.

3   Amino acids contain carbon (C), nitrogen (N), oxygen (O) and hydrogen (H) atoms, and some contain an atom of sulfur (S).

4   There are about 20 different amino acids, with different side chains (R groups).

5   Amino acids are linked via peptide bonds to make polypeptides and proteins.

6   Each protein molecule can be hundreds of amino acids long and the amino acids must be joined in a precise order, which is specified by a code in the DNA in the chromosomes.

7   The side-chains (R groups) of the amino acids can interact with one another to fold the protein into a particular shape which is essential for the protein to function correctly.

8   When protein food is eaten, the amino acids are released by the activity of peptidase enzymes during digestion. The amino acids are then absorbed into the blood and used to build up the body's own proteins.

9   The amount of protein needed in a balanced diet differs according to age and gender. Insufficient or excess protein in the diet can cause health problems.

Answer to Activity SP4.1

Figure SP4.10 shows two possible ways in which the information on protein digestion can be summarised, though your version could be just as good, or even better, and be quite different from either of these.

Answer to Activity SP4.2

(a) Your table might look something like Table SP4.6, though you may have chosen to put the EAR and RNI values as the row headings and the different genders and ages as the columns, which is just as good. The data for women between 19 and 50 is given in the preceding text.

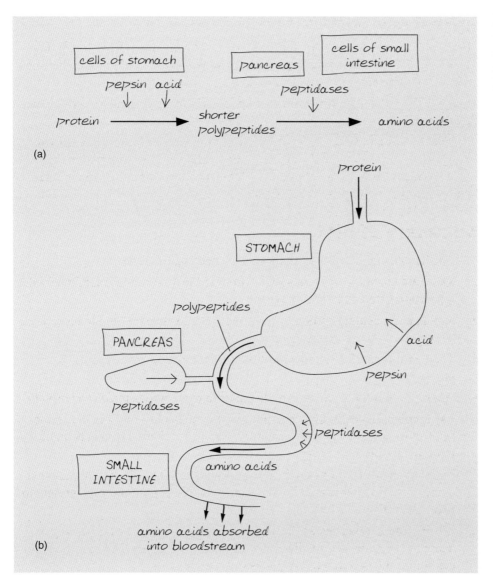

Figure SP4.10 Two possible ways of summarising information on protein digestion: (a) a flow chart, and (b) a diagram.

Table SP4.6 Dietary reference values for protein for adults.

Gender and age	Estimated average requirement, EAR/g per day	Reference nutrient intake, RNI/g per day
Men		
19–50 years	44.4	55.5
over 50 years	42.6	53.3
Women		
19–50 years	36.0	45.0
over 50 years	37.2	46.5

(b) Your answer to this part will depend on the person you chose and their diet. If they ate foods which are rather different from those given in Table SP4.2, you may not have been able to estimate the daily protein intake very accurately. Here is an example:

Meal	Food eaten	Estimated protein content/g
Breakfast	Cereal with milk (8 g per 40 g serving, with milk, according to packet)	8
Lunch	White bread, 100 g (8% protein)	8
	Cheese, 50 g (26% protein)	13
	A little butter (less than 1% protein)	negligible
	6 cherry tomatoes	unknown
	Piece of fruit cake	unknown
	Banana, 120 g fruit (1% protein)	1.2
Evening meal	Beef stew, made with 150 g beef (20% protein)	30
	Baked potato, 150 g (2% protein)	3
	Frozen green beans, 75 g (1.3 g per 75 g serving, according to packet)	1.3
	Yoghurt, 150 g (5 g protein per 100 g)	7.5
Hot drinks	Made with about 150 ml milk (about 150 g, with 3.4 g protein per 100 g, according to carton)	5.1
Snack	Apple, 100 g (less than 1% protein); cheese, 25 g (26% protein)	about 6
	Total protein	about 83

This person (female, over 50) has eaten about 83 g protein during this day, significantly more than both the estimated average requirement (EAR) of 37.2 g protein and the reference nutrient intake (RNI) of 46.5 g protein. It is also more than the 71.3 g estimated daily protein intake in the UK determined by the Expenditure and Food Survey, referred to in Question SP4.2, but less than the safe limit of 90 g per day, calculated in Question SP4.3 for a woman weighing 60 kg.

Fats

5.1   Introduction

As well as discussing the fats and oils in our diet, which are chemically very similar, this study period covers some related compounds called phospholipids and steroids, and also lipoproteins which are aggregates of fat and protein found in the bloodstream. The general term 'lipids' includes all of these compounds. All cells contain lipids as a major component of their membranes and many animals and plants use stores of fat or oil to provide energy when needed.

5.2   Fats and oils

Question SP5.1 Based on what you might find in your kitchen or on the supermarket shelves, list at least five examples of fats and five examples of oils.

5.2.1   Physical characteristics of fats and oils

● What are the characteristic features of fats and oils, which you could use to tell them apart from other substances?

◌ Fats and oils have a slippery feel when you touch them and they do not dissolve in water.

● When drawing up your list in answer to Question SP5.1, how did you decide which was a fat and which was an oil?

◌ Most people use the term 'fats' for those that are solid, or semi-solid at room temperature, and 'oils' for those that are liquid at room temperature. However, 'room temperature' does vary and while, for example, coconut oil would generally be solid in the UK, it is liquid in the tropical countries where coconuts grow.

● Look again at your list. What do you notice about the sources of the fats compared with the sources of the oils?

◌ Most of the fats come from animals and most of the oils come from plants. However, there are exceptions. One of the oils (cod liver oil) is derived from fish. Margarine is a manufactured product that can be made from fats and oils from a mix of sources, chemically treated in various ways and with added ingredients such as vitamins and colouring. You will see a lengthy list of ingredients on the packaging.

● Next time you have the opportunity, you might like to try mixing two tablespoons of oil and one tablespoon of vinegar to make a salad dressing. Put the liquids into a small screw-topped jar and shake them gently. Then place the jar on a surface and watch what happens. Next, try shaking (or whisking) the mixture more vigorously for a couple of minutes and watch the contents again when the jar is still. Finally add about half a teaspoon of dry mustard powder to the mix, shake again and watch what happens.

● You should have seen that the oil and vinegar form two quite separate layers, with vinegar, which is mostly water, at the bottom, and the oil on top. If shaken gently, the oil breaks up into droplets, but then the two layers separate out again quite quickly. If shaken for longer or whisked, the oil breaks up into very tiny droplets, the dressing begins to take on a milky appearance and the layers take longer to separate out. This milky mixture is an emulsion. Addition of the mustard powder stabilises the emulsion (as well as adding flavour!) and it takes very much longer for the two layers to reappear. With the addition of some herbs and black pepper, you will have a very tasty salad dressing.

Oil and water do not mix completely, but form an emulsion of one in the other. If the droplets in the mixture are small enough, the emulsion may take days to separate out. Milk is a good example of this type of emulsion. It is the tiny fat droplets that produce the 'milky' appearance.

● What word describes the 'water-hating' property of fats and oils?

● The word is 'hydrophobic', which you met in SP4.6.1.

> You may not have remembered this word, but you should have been able to find it quite quickly, either because you had highlighted it in the book, because you had included it in your notes or in your personal glossary, or by looking in the *Course Glossary*. One of the important skills we are hoping to develop here is that of being able quickly to find information that you have already met. A lot of people equate 'cleverness' with 'having a good memory' when in fact, the really 'clever' people are those who can find the information they require quickly and don't need to bother remembering it!

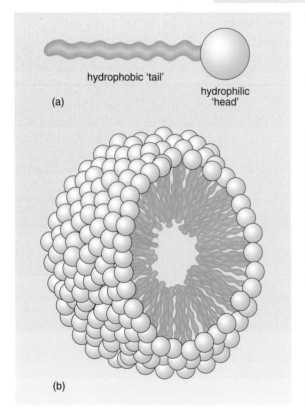

hydrophobic 'tail'

hydrophilic 'head'

(a)

(b)

● If fats do not dissolve in water, how can the remains of fatty foods be washed away with water from plates and cooking utensils?

● The most effective way of removing fat (i.e. making it dissolve in water) is by using a detergent (washing-up liquid) in the water.

Molecules of detergent are rather special. They have a hydrophilic 'head' and a hydrophobic 'tail' (Figure SP5.1a). When detergent molecules encounter a droplet of fat, the hydrophobic tails embed themselves in between the fat molecules, which are also hydrophobic. Their hydrophilic heads lie away from the fat droplet and in contact with the water. Thus a minute sphere is formed with the fat in the centre (Figure SP5.1b). These little spheres then float away in the water, so removing the fat from the plates and cooking utensils.

Figure SP5.1 (a) Schematic representation of a detergent molecule. (b) Detergent molecules surrounding a fat droplet, with their 'tails' embedded in the fat.

5.3 Chemical structure of fats and oils

Fats and oils have a common chemical structure and so the word 'fat' will be used from now on to include oils too, unless otherwise stated. Fats contain the elements carbon (C), hydrogen (H) and oxygen (O).

● How does this list of elements differ from the list of elements found in proteins?

◔ Proteins also contain nitrogen (N) (see Figure SP4.3).

5.3.1 Glycerol

Each molecule of fat is a combination of one molecule of glycerol and three molecules of substances called fatty acids. Glycerol is a liquid and is also known as glycerine. (Although it ends in '-ine', glycerine is not an amino acid.) It is an ingredient of some cough medication, since it is sweet and smooth tasting and soothing to the throat. A molecule of glycerol has three carbon atoms attached together in a row, an $-OH$ group (one oxygen atom with one hydrogen atom) attached to each carbon and the rest of the bonds of the carbon atoms taken up with single hydrogen atoms.

● Draw a glycerol molecule from the description above, writing the carbon atoms in a vertical column, rather than a horizontal row. You may need to check back to SP4.4 Table SP4.4 to recall how many bonds (arms) each type of atom must have.

◔ The structure of glycerol is shown opposite. You may have drawn the molecule with the $-OH$ groups to the left of the carbon atoms, which is equally correct. If you were able to draw this molecule, then congratulations – you obviously have a good understanding of the chemistry.

5.3.2 Palmitic acid

The other components of fats are fatty acids, which are much bigger than glycerol. Here is the structure of one member of the fatty acid family called palmitic acid:

$$CH_3-CH_2-CH_2-CH_2-CH_2-CH_2-CH_2-CH_2-CH_2-CH_2-CH_2-CH_2-CH_2-CH_2-CH_2-C \overset{O}{\underset{OH}{}}$$

You could, if you wish, draw this molecule out in full, with the hydrogen atoms each attached by a separate bond to their carbon atoms. That would show you that, as ever, each H atom has one bond and each C atom has four bonds. At the right-hand end of the molecule is a $-COOH$ group.

● What is the name of this $-COOH$ group? Check back to SP4.4 if you don't remember, though the name of the molecule gives you a broad hint.

◔ $-COOH$ is a carboxylic acid group.

● How many $-CH_2-$ groups does the palmitic acid molecule have in its long tail?

● There are 14 $-CH_2-$ groups and, rather than writing each one out separately, we can summarise that part of the molecule as $-(CH_2)_{14}-$.

So, with the CH_3- group at one end and the $-COOH$ group at the other, a quicker way to write out the structure of a palmitic acid molecule would be $CH_3(CH_2)_{14}COOH$.

● Use this shortened representation to count how many of each type of atom are present in a palmitic acid molecule. You could check your answer by counting on the extended version given earlier.

● There are, in total, 16 carbon atoms, 32 hydrogen atoms and two oxygen atoms. However, if you add them together and try to write palmitic acid as $C_{16}H_{32}O_2$, then you lose a lot of information. You can no longer see that it has a long chain of carbon atoms, each with two hydrogen atoms attached, with a CH_3- group on one end and a $-COOH$ group on the other. So, you should not add the numbers of atoms together like this when you are representing a fatty acid, or any other similar molecule.

All fatty acids have a similar basic structure, with the long tail of carbon atoms, and a $-COOH$ group at one end. Fats are often called triacylglycerols (pronounced 'try-ay-sile-gliss-er-rols'), sometimes abbreviated to TAGs. You may also see them referred to by the older term triglycerides (pronounced 'try-gliss-er-ides').

● What information does the word 'triacylglycerol' tell you about the chemical make-up of a fat molecule?

● You should recognise 'tri-' as meaning that the molecule contains three of something – in this case, three fatty acids – that's the '-acyl-' part, which is similar to the word acid. Then 'glycerol' is the name of the molecule that makes up the rest of the fat.

5.3.3 Linking glycerol and fatty acids

The next task is to link the fatty acids and the glycerol together to make fat.

● When two amino acids are linked together, which small molecule is removed, in order that the link can be made? You may need to look back to Figure SP4.4.

● A molecule of water is produced, by removing $-OH$ from the carboxylic acid $-COOH$ group and an $-H$ from the $-NH_2$ group and combining them together to make H_2O.

The same kind of reaction can occur to link fatty acids to glycerol, though this time the $-H$ comes from the $-OH$ group of glycerol, as shown in Figure SP5.2a. Note that the palmitic acid molecule here has been drawn with the $-COOH$ group on the left. Three fatty acids need to be added to make a complete triacylglycerol molecule (Figure SP5.2b).

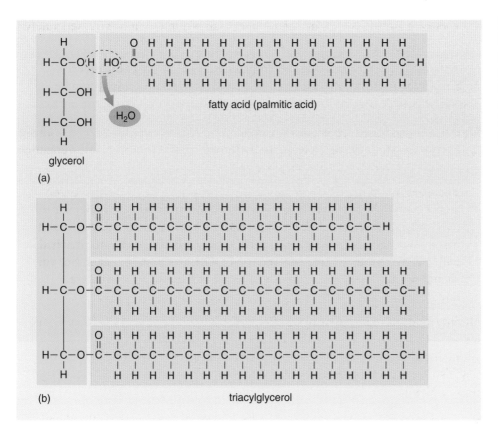

Figure SP5.2 (a) The reaction in which one molecule of fatty acid is added to a molecule of glycerol. (b) A triacylglycerol molecule formed by the addition of three molecules of fatty acid to a molecule of glycerol.

● How many water molecules are produced when a complete triacylglycerol (fat) molecule is made?

◍ Since each time a fatty acid is linked to glycerol, one water molecule is produced, a total of three molecules are produced when a complete triacylglycerol molecule is produced from glycerol and three fatty acids.

You might be wondering what happens to these water molecules. All living cells contain a high proportion of water, so wherever the fat is made, these extra molecules of water just add to the amount already in the cells.

5.3.4 Different fatty acids

Palmitic acid is found in the seeds of the oil palm and coconut palm, as you might have guessed from its name. It is one of a group of fatty acids that differ in various ways, including having a different length of tail and therefore a different number of carbon atoms in the molecule as a whole. However, because fatty acids are built up from small molecules that contain two carbon atoms, most of those produced by animals and plants have an even number of carbon atoms.

● Look back to the structure of palmitic acid. Does it have an even number of carbon atoms?

◍ Yes it does. There are 16: 14 in the main part of the chain, one in the CH_3- group at one end and one in the $-COOH$ group at the other.

Activity SP5.1

During the rest of this section, you will be filling in the information about fatty acids into the partly completed Table SP5.1. Start with palmitic acid in the fourth row, by filling in its source and the number of carbon atoms it contains. Don't worry about the last three columns for the moment.

Table SP5.1 Names and properties of a selection of fatty acids, for completion during SP5.

Name of fatty acid	Source	No. of carbon atoms	Saturation	No. of carbon-to-carbon double bonds	Fatty acid 'family'
		4			
		12			
		14			
palmitic					
		18			
		20			
			monounsaturated		
		20			
		20			
		22			

There are fatty acids with fewer carbon atoms than palmitic. Those with six or fewer carbon atoms are called 'short-chain' fatty acids. One of them is butyric acid, which is found in butter (*butyrum* is Latin for 'butter') and has four carbon atoms. Fatty acids with between eight and 12 carbon atoms are 'medium-chain' fatty acids. Lauric acid, named after the laurel plant, and also found in butter, has 12 carbons. Add these two examples to the appropriate rows in Table SP5.1 too.

From 14 carbons onwards, the fatty acids are called 'long-chain' and since about 95% of the fats we eat contain long-chain fatty acids, we shall concentrate on those. The fatty acid similar to palmitic but with only 14 carbon atoms is myristic acid (named after nutmeg, genus *Myristica*), the one with 18 is stearic acid, and the one with 20 is arachidic acid. All three of these are found in butter, though analysis shows that the most common fatty acid in butter is stearic acid. Stearic acid is also found in beef fat, in lard and in hard margarine. Arachidic acid is in peanuts. Add these fatty acids and their details to Table SP5.1.

All of the fatty acids so far have single bonds between each of the carbon atoms and are said to be saturated, so you can write that in the 'Saturation' column next to each of them, and put a zero in the 'Number of carbon-to-carbon double bonds' column, since they do not have any. They do not belong to a particular family, so leave the 'Fatty acid 'family'' column blank.

● The fatty acid shown below is called oleic acid, and forms nearly three-quarters of the fatty acids in olive oil (though it occurs very widely, and forms a significant percentage of the fatty acids in cod liver oil too). How many carbon atoms does it have? What differences are there between its structure and the structure of a saturated fatty acid like palmitic acid or stearic acid?

$CH_3-CH_2-CH_2-CH_2-CH_2-CH_2-CH_2-CH_2-CH=CH-CH_2-CH_2-CH_2-CH_2-CH_2-CH_2-CH_2-COOH$

◉ Oleic acid has 18 carbon atoms, which is the same total as stearic acid. But whereas stearic acid has single bonds between all its carbon atoms, oleic acid has a double bond between the ninth and tenth carbon atoms, counting from the CH_3- end (so it also has two fewer hydrogen atoms). In fact, the double bond is exactly in the middle of the carbon chain and so it is between the ninth and tenth carbon atoms if you count from the $-COOH$ end too. However, in other fatty acids with one double bond, it may not be exactly in the middle and the convention is that the counting always starts at the CH_3- end.

Double bonds were introduced towards the end of SP4.2. Remember each carbon atom must have four bonds. So, if we look at the centre of the oleic acid molecule in detail, the bonds are arranged as shown here.

So the centre two carbon atoms are each 'holding two hands' with each other, and 'one hand' to the carbon on the other side leaving 'one hand' free to bond to one hydrogen atom. Fatty acids (and other molecules) which contain double bonds in the carbon chain are said to be unsaturated. If there is just one double bond in the carbon chain, as in oleic acid, then the fatty acid is said to be monounsaturated. Since the double bond is attached to the ninth carbon, oleic acid, which is the most common monounsaturated fatty acid, belongs to the *n*-9 family of fatty acids, also known as omega 9. (Omega is a Greek letter written in lower case as ω.) Now add oleic acid and all its details to Table SP5.1, in the row containing 'monounsaturated'.

● Recalling the method used for palmitic acid, write the formula of oleic acid in a more abbreviated form. You will need to leave the centre carbons with the double bonds as they are, but combine the $-CH_2-$ groups on either side.

◉ Oleic acid is written as

$CH_3(CH_2)_7CH=CH(CH_2)_7COOH$

Remember that you should not add up all the atoms and group them together when writing the formula of a compound like this.

If a fatty acid has more than one double bond (even if there are only two) it is called polyunsaturated. Polyunsaturated fatty acids can be abbreviated to PUFAs.

● Below is the formula of linoleic acid which is found very widely, including in some meats, eggs, nuts and many oils. How many carbon atoms does it have and which carbon atom has the first double bond attached to it (counting from the CH_3- end)? Write its formula in the abbreviated form too.

$CH_3-CH_2-CH_2-CH_2-CH_2-CH=CH-CH_2-CH=CH-CH_2-CH_2-CH_2-CH_2-CH_2-CH_2-CH_2-COOH$

◉ Linoleic acid has 18 carbon atoms, with the first double bond on the sixth carbon atom. Its formula can be written as

$CH_3(CH_2)_4CH=CHCH_2CH=CH(CH_2)_7COOH$

So here we have a fatty acid with the same number of carbon atoms as oleic acid, but with an extra double bond, so it is polyunsaturated. The family to which a polyunsaturated fatty acid belongs depends on the position of the first double bond, counting from the CH_3- end. So this one belongs to the n-6 or omega 6 family. Add it to the next line of Table SP5.1, below oleic acid.

Finally in the group with 18 carbon atoms is linolenic acid (also called alpha-linolenic acid). Here is its abbreviated formula:

$CH_3CH_2CH=CHCH_2CH=CHCH_2CH=CH(CH_2)_7COOH$

● Apart from the very subtle difference in name, what other differences are there between linolenic and linoleic acid?

◉ Linolenic acid has a third double bond, near the start of the molecule. This double bond is attached to the third carbon, making it a member of the very important family of n-3 or omega 3 fatty acids. Note that the '3' in n-3 refers to the position of the first double bond and not to the number of double bonds present. The rest of the molecule is the same in both acids.

Add linolenic acid on the row below linoleic in Table SP5.1. Linolenic acid is also found in a wide range of foods, including dark green leafy vegetables, as well as nuts and the oils derived from them, and in smaller quantities in poultry meat.

Finally, the last three and longest fatty acids in Table SP5.1 are arachidonic acid (20 carbons, four double bonds, n-6 family, found in plant oils, especially peanuts), eicosapentaenoic acid (EPA) (20 carbons, five double bonds, n-3 family) and docosahexaenoic acid (DHA) (22 carbons, 6 double bonds, n-3 family). The long-chain fatty acids from the n-3 (omega 3) family are widespread in oily fish such as sardines, salmon, trout, mackerel and tuna, and in many plants and seeds. Add information on these three fatty acids to complete Table SP5.1 and then compare your completed Table SP5.1 with Table SP5.4 at the end of this study period.

5.3.5 Mixed fatty acids

In this section, you will need to be able to read data from a bar chart. If you are not familiar with bar charts, you should read the relevant section in the *Maths Skills Booklet* before you go any further.

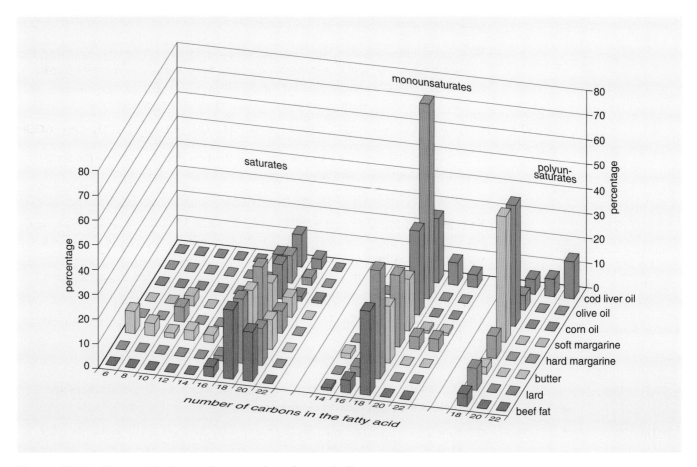

Figure SP5.3 Fatty acids that make up various fats and oils.

Figure SP5.3 shows the range of fatty acids that are used to make up the triacylglycerol molecules of particular fats and oils. This three-dimensional bar chart is quite difficult to read, so you will probably need to work through the following description slowly and carefully. The number of carbon atoms in each fatty acid is written along the front of the diagram and then the names of the fats and oils present in the diet are given to the right. A coloured flat square indicates none (or very little) of that fatty acid in that fat. So, for example, polyunsaturated fatty acids with 20 and 22 carbon atoms in the two rows running from front to back on the far right of the chart do not occur in any of the fats and oils shown except for cod liver oil. Where a given fatty acid does occur in a particular fat, there is a vertical column, the height of which indicates the average percentage present. The percentage can be read off on the scale up the left-hand side, which also continues along the back of the chart. So, for example, olive oil contains more than 70% of a monounsaturated fatty acid with 18 carbons – the tall green column. Butter, the yellow row, contains a range of fatty acids but insignificant amounts of saturated fatty acids with 22 carbons, and mono- and polyunsaturated ones with 20 and 22 carbons (the flat yellow squares).

The way that the data about fatty acids in different fats and oils are presented masks another complication. Each molecule of triacylglycerol can contain three identical fatty acids joined to the glycerol. However, much more commonly in natural triacylglycerols, a molecule contains two or three different fatty acids, as shown in Figure SP5.2b.

The mix of fatty acids that are combined in each triacylglycerol molecule and the range of types of triacylglycerol determine the properties of the fat or oil in the tissues of particular species that synthesise them.

Question SP5.2 Use the information from Figure SP5.3 and your completed version of Table SP5.1 to answer the following questions about the fatty acids found in fats and oils.

(a) Which is the most widely occurring saturated fatty acid?

(b) What do you notice about the most widely occurring fatty acid in each of the three groups – saturates, monounsaturates and polyunsaturates?

(c) Which two food items each contain about 50% of an 18-carbon polyunsaturated fatty acid? You might find it useful to measure the height of the column and compare it with the scale.

(d) What do you notice about the range of fatty acids found in hard fats, compared with those found in oils? ◀

Question SP5.3 (a) On each of the triacylglycerol molecules in Figure SP5.4, circle the part that is derived from glycerol. You may find it useful to look back to Figure SP5.2.

(b) Count how many carbon atoms are present in each of the fatty acids in the triacylglycerol molecules in Figure SP5.4a and b, and so identify the fatty acids, using your completed version of Table SP5.1. ◀

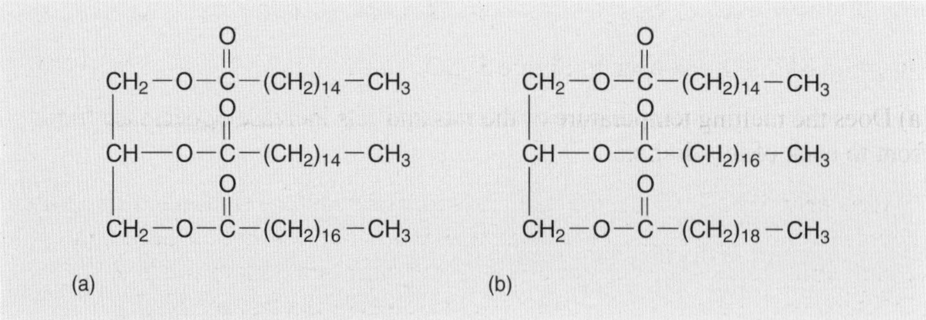

Figure SP5.4 Two of the triacylglycerols found in butter.

(a)

(b)

5.3.6 Melting temperatures

A solid substance consists of molecules that are held quite firmly in place by attractive forces between the molecules. When a substance is heated sufficiently for it to melt, the molecules have gained enough energy to overcome these forces and the molecules are much freer to move around; the substance becomes a liquid. The strength of the forces holding the molecules together in a solid depends on various factors, but the two that are important for fats and oils are the length and the shape of the fatty acid tails.

The attractive forces are larger between larger molecules, so more energy (heat) is needed to overcome these forces. Thus fats with more carbon atoms in their fatty acid chains generally have higher melting temperatures than those with fewer carbon atoms. For example, a synthetic triacylglycerol made with three stearic acids (each with 18 carbon atoms) has a much higher melting temperature than a similar molecule with three butyric acids (each with only four carbon atoms).

So far, the fatty acids have been drawn as a straight chain but the introduction of a double bond into the chain puts a bend into it. If the remaining single hydrogen atoms on the carbons at each end of the double bond are on the same side, then the arrangement is termed *cis*. If they are on opposite sides, then the arrangement is *trans* (*trans* means 'across', as in trans-Atlantic). These two possible arrangements are shown in Figure SP5.5.

● Which of the two arrangements, *cis* or *trans*, introduces a larger bend into the fatty acid chain?

● The *cis* arrangement introduces the larger bend. In a fatty acid with a *trans* double bond, there is just a slight offset in the fatty acid chain.

Most of the naturally occurring fatty acids are of the *cis* variety, but *trans* fatty acids are produced during the manufacture of hard margarine and so are found in cakes, biscuits and pastry made from such margarine. They are also produced by the bacteria that live in the stomachs of ruminant animals like cows and sheep, so meat and dairy products from these animals will also contain *trans* fatty acids. There is some evidence that *trans* fatty acids can have adverse health consequences, as you will see in SP14.

Fatty acids with more double bonds, and in particular with more *cis* double bonds, will have more bends and so triacylglycerols made from such fatty acids will not be able to line up as closely alongside one another. The molecules do not 'pack' so neatly together. Thus the forces holding them together will not be so great, so they will form liquids more easily; they will have lower melting temperatures.

Question SP5.4 Look back to Figure SP5.3.

(a) Does the melting temperature of the fats and oils increase or decrease from front to back of this diagram?

(b) Concentrate now on just the part of the bar chart on the right-hand side, which shows the polyunsaturates (fatty acids with more than one double bond). In general terms, how does the proportion of polyunsaturated fatty acids in triacylglycerols relate to the melting temperatures of the fats and oils?

(c) How does the relationship between fatty acid composition of triacylglycerols and their melting temperature relate to the way that the molecules 'pack' together? ◀

Natural fats generally contain not only a mix of fatty acids in each of their triacylglycerol molecules (as shown in Figure SP5.4), but also a variety of triacylglycerols, some with one set of fatty acids, some with another set, and so

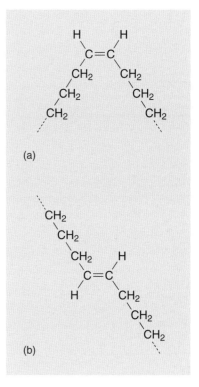

(a)

(b)

Figure SP5.5 Arrangement of atoms on either side of (a) a *cis* double bond and (b) a *trans* double bond.

on. This mix results in the different triacylglycerols separating from one another at different temperatures and means that fats (and oils) do not have a precise melting temperature, but melt over a range of temperatures. As the temperature is raised, the triacylglycerols with the lower melting temperatures melt first, then as the temperature increases further, those with higher melting temperatures begin to melt. So at any one temperature within that range, the fat is not completely solid, neither is it completely runny like a liquid. Being a mixture of various triacylglycerols contributes to making fats like butter and soft margarine 'spreadable' on bread, for example. The fat actually consists of solid particles of the triacylglycerols with the higher melting temperatures, in a matrix of viscous (thick) liquid made up of the triacylglycerols with the lower melting temperatures. A solid material with spreading properties is thus produced, in which the more liquid parts help the solid components to slide over one another.

Question SP5.5 Butter is hard when taken out of the fridge (at about 4 °C) but then is soft enough to spread when it warms up to room temperature (about 20 °C), whereas soft margarine can be spread straight from the fridge and changes very little in softness if allowed to warm up to room temperature. What can you deduce from this information about the melting temperatures of the triacylglycerols in each of them? ◄

5.3.7 Chocolate

Chocolate is made from cocoa, cocoa butter and sugar. Cocoa butter is made up of only a few different types of triacylglycerol molecules, so it has quite a sharp, well defined melting temperature. In fact the molecules can pack together in several different ways. One of these forms melts at 33.8 °C. Thus it melts in your mouth (36.9 °C) but not in your hand, which is usually cooler. This form is also smooth and glossy. To persuade it to solidify in this form, the melted chocolate is cooled and maintained at just below 33.8 °C. It is also stirred so that the fat crystallises into very small crystals, which gives chocolate its velvety texture. If chocolate is subject to fluctuations in temperature, a bloom develops on the surface. Contrary to popular belief, this is not mould but is the fat solidifying in different crystalline forms.

5.3.8 Essential fatty acids

Our bodies can synthesise most of the fatty acids we need, but not quite all of them. Linoleic acid and (alpha) linolenic acid are the two essential fatty acids. However, as you will see by reference back to Table SP5.1, they are both widely available in common foods and so deficiency is rare in people eating a normal varied diet. Both these fatty acids are essential components of the phospholipids that form cell membranes (see SP5.4.1) and are used to produce molecules called eicosanoids. Eicosanoids act as signalling molecules between cells and can affect certain aspects of body function such as blood pressure, blood clotting, inflammation and maintenance of body temperature.

5.4   Other lipids

As well as the fats and oils already considered, which are all lipids, there are various other types of lipid with rather different structures.

5.4.1 Phospholipids

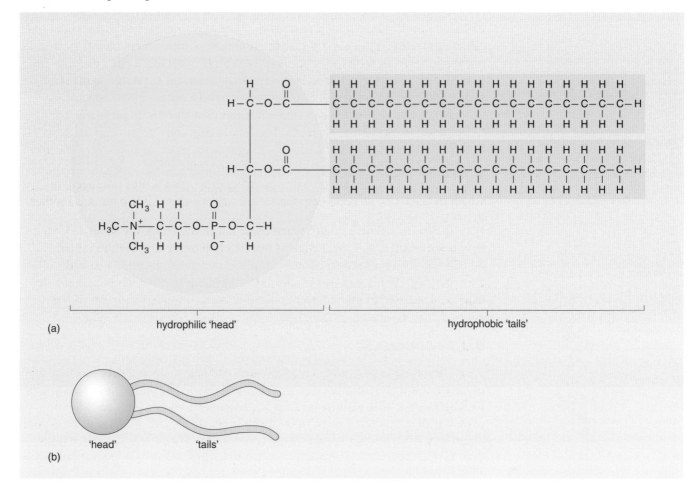

Figure SP5.6 (a) Structural formula of a phospholipid molecule. (b) Diagrammatic representation of a phospholipid molecule.

● Look carefully at Figure SP5.6, which shows a phospholipid molecule and compare it with Figure SP5.2b. In what ways is the phospholipid molecule similar to a triacylglycerol molecule, and in what ways is it different?

◐ It is similar in that the 'core' of the molecule consists of a glycerol molecule (the three carbon atoms shown in a column). Attached to that are fatty acid 'tails', as in a triacylglycerol molecule, but there are only two fatty acids in the phospholipid molecule, not three. Instead of the third fatty acid, the phospholipid has a group of atoms attached which includes an atom of phosphorus (P), hence the 'phospho-' in the name. This group also contains a nitrogen atom which carries a positive charge (shown as +), and an oxygen atom which carries a negative charge (shown as −), as well as having carbon, hydrogen and other oxygen atoms. You may recall that some of the R groups of amino acids also carry charges (Table SP4.5).

The presence of charged atoms and the additional oxygen atoms in the phospholipid 'head' make the head soluble in water (hydrophilic), while the

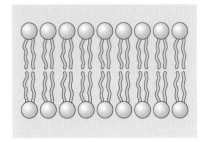

Figure SP5.7 A phospholipid bilayer, which forms the structural part of cell membranes.

'tails', composed only of carbon and hydrogen atoms, are hydrophobic. Phospholipid molecules line up to form a double layer, called a bilayer, with their heads on the outside and their tails on the inside (Figure SP5.7). Such phospholipid bilayers are the main structural component of biological membranes, which form the boundaries of cells (Figure SP1.1) and many of the internal components too. They are particularly abundant in the brain and other parts of the nervous system. Phospholipids can be synthesised in the body, so they are not essential in the diet (though their constituent fatty acids can be).

5.4.2 Cholesterol

A cholesterol molecule has a complex structure based on four rings of carbon atoms, three with six carbon atoms and one with five.

● Which other molecules have you met that contain rings of six carbon atoms?

○ Cyclohexane and benzene (SP4.2) are both single rings of six carbon atoms with hydrogen atoms attached. The amino acid phenylalanine (Table SP4.5) has a ring similar to benzene, attached as part of its side-chain (R group).

Although cholesterol has a bad press because of its tendency to form plaques that can ultimately block arteries, it does, in fact, have at least three essential roles in the body. Firstly, it is a component of cell membranes and plays an important part in stabilising their structure. It is also needed to produce bile salts, important in the absorption of fats from the digestive system into the blood. And finally, various hormones, including the sex hormones, other important steroids and vitamin D all require cholesterol in their synthesis.

In humans, all cells can synthesise cholesterol, but, in general, the amount they produce is insufficient for their needs, and additional cholesterol is synthesised by the liver and transported to the rest of the body in the blood. When blood cholesterol levels are high, for example if the dietary intake is high, cholesterol synthesis by the liver is reduced. Thus under 'normal' circumstances, cholesterol levels appear to be kept within an appropriate range and, contrary to popular belief, variations in dietary intake of cholesterol do not, for most individuals, have much effect on blood cholesterol levels. Possible links between cholesterol and the development of coronary heart disease will be explored further in SP14.

5.4.3 Lipoproteins

Lipoproteins, aggregates of fat (triacylglycerols) and protein, are used to transport fat around the body in the blood.

● Remembering its hydrophobic nature, suggest why fat cannot be transported around simply as triacylglycerol molecules in the blood.

○ Since triacylglycerol molecules are hydrophobic (water-hating), they do not dissolve in the water-based blood and could separate out into droplets.

So for transport around the body in the blood, triacylglycerol molecules are associated with protein molecules, and since the aggregates contain much more fat than protein and fat has a low density, they are called very low-density lipoproteins (VLDLs). VLDLs also contain cholesterol. They are formed in the liver and then secreted into the bloodstream. The fate of the VLDLs from here onwards is illustrated in Figure SP5.8. You should follow the stages in the figure as you read the text.

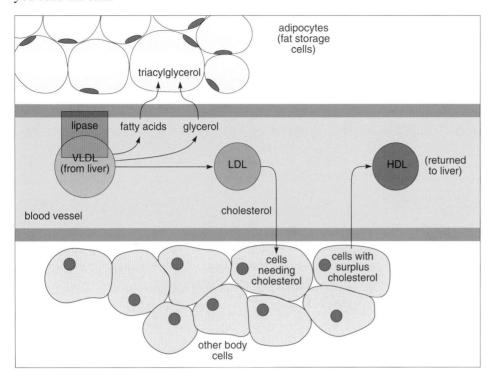

Figure SP5.8 Summary diagram showing lipoprotein and cholesterol transport.

If the triacylglycerols are not needed immediately, they can be stored in special cells called adipose cells or adipocytes. The tissue composed mainly of these fat-storage cells is called adipose tissue (or, if present on meat, or in the human body, it is often just called 'fat'). To get the triacylglycerols from the blood into these cells, they would need to pass out through the walls of the blood capillaries, but the intact fat molecules are too big. A fat-digesting enzyme, lipoprotein lipase, is secreted by the adipocytes and becomes anchored in the blood vessel wall where it breaks down the VLDLs, freeing the fatty acids from the glycerol. These components are then small enough to be absorbed separately into the adipocytes where they are re-combined into triacylglycerols for storage.

As the triacylglycerols are gradually removed from the VLDLs, the proportion of protein and cholesterol the VLDLs are carrying increases and their density increases, until they become low-density lipoproteins or LDLs. If cells need cholesterol for repairing or building new membranes, then specific molecules on the outside of the cells bind to the protein part of the LDLs, and the cholesterol is taken up by the cells. Those cells that contain more cholesterol than needed, export it back to the liver in the form of high-density lipoproteins, HDLs. It is the ratio of LDL cholesterol to HDL cholesterol in the blood that is thought to be the best indicator of the risk of developing coronary heart disease; the greater the proportion of HDL, the lower the risk. Diet, smoking and exercise all appear to affect HDL levels. Blood tests to measure cholesterol levels are widely available.

Question SP5.6 Identify which of the following statements are false and for each, identify the error:

(a) Phospholipids, cholesterol and lipoproteins are all important components of cell membranes.

(b) Lipoproteins are a combination of fats and proteins.

(c) Triacylglycerols are soluble in blood.

(d) VLDLs contain more cholesterol than LDLs.

(e) High levels of LDL cholesterol reduce the risk of coronary heart disease. ◄

5.5 Digestion and absorption of fat

The family of enzymes that digest fat are called lipases. You have already met lipoprotein lipase (SP5.4.3). Lipases in the digestive tract which break down fats in the diet, mostly triacylglycerols, are produced mainly by the pancreas. In babies, a small amount of lipase is produced in the saliva in the mouth, aiding the digestion of the lipids in milk, and breastfed infants obtain some lipase from the milk itself. (Lipases are also present in animal milk but are often destroyed by processing.) However, in adults, no actual digestion of fat begins until it reaches the small intestine. In the stomach, the fat is simply churned around with the rest of the food, though its presence does appear to stimulate the production of a group of hormones that slow down the rate at which the stomach empties. Consequently, a fatty meal usually remains in the stomach for longer than a non-fatty one, giving a feeling of fullness (satiety) that lasts longer.

● Look back to HN Figure 2.1 p. 19. How does the presence of food in the stomach produce the feeling of satiety?

◌ The food causes the stomach to be stretched (gastric distension), which is detected by stretch receptors. The information passed via nerves to the brain reduces the feeling of hunger (indicated by the minus sign in HN Figure 2.1).

The processing of the fatty components of food once they reach the small intestine is illustrated in Figure SP5.9 and, as with Figure SP5.8, you should follow the processes on the figure as you read the text. The fat is first acted upon by enzymes from the pancreas and by bile from the gall bladder (Figure SP2.2b). Bile is produced by the liver, and stored in the bile ducts and gall bladder until its release into the gut. It contains bile salts (also called bile acids, because they are acidic salts), the molecules of which have a hydrophobic 'tail' and a hydrophilic 'head', along with cholesterol.

● How might interaction between triacylglycerols and bile salts affect the droplets of fat? Consider the similarity with the way detergents act on fats (Figure SP5.1).

◌ Like a detergent, the hydrophobic 'tails' of the bile salt molecules embed themselves in the droplets of fat, with their hydrophilic 'heads' sticking out towards the watery contents of the intestine. They thus surround the fat droplets and prevent tiny droplets re-aggregating into larger ones.

So the effect of the bile is to emulsify the fat into many very small droplets which in total have a much greater surface area than one large droplet, and so the digestive enzyme lipase can work more efficiently. Lipase is secreted into the small intestine from the pancreas and it acts on the triacylglycerols by splitting off two of the three fatty acids, leaving a monoacylglycerol.

● What are the components of a monoacylglycerol?

◌ A monoacylglycerol has just one fatty acid attached to the glycerol molecule.

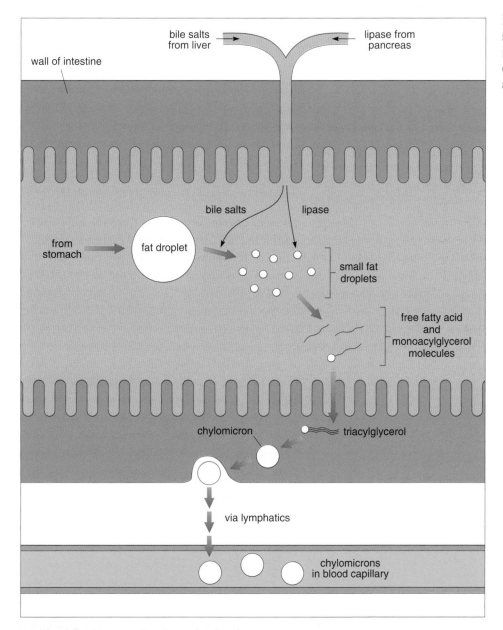

Figure SP5.9 A diagrammatic section of part of the small intestine to show the processes of emulsification, digestion and absorption of fats (not to scale).

The monoacylglycerol and the individual ('free') fatty acids are small enough to pass through the cell membrane and into the cells of the lining of the small intestine, known as the intestinal epithelium. These cells are the ones with the 'ruffled' edge drawn in Figure SP1.1. Once inside these cells, the triacylglycerol molecules are reassembled and, together with cholesterol and fat-soluble vitamins also present in the food, they are coated with phospholipids and lipoproteins, to make tiny composite lipoprotein droplets called chylomicrons. These chylomicrons are then expelled from the other side of the cell and eventually find their way into the bloodstream via the lymphatic system, which you will meet again in SP14. Once in the blood, the chylomicrons mix with the other blood lipoproteins. Chylomicrons are the largest and lightest of the various types of lipoproteins and are processed in the same way as the VLDLs.

5.6 Dietary fat

Many fatty foods taste pleasant to humans and UK intake is high. Dietary advice, on health grounds, has led to a decrease in fat intake in recent years and a switch away from saturated fats towards monounsaturated and polyunsaturated plant and fish oils, as shown in Table SP5.2.

Table SP5.2 Mean total fat intake in the UK per person per day, together with the percentage of total energy in the diet obtained from the different types of fatty acids, 1970–2000.

Year	Total fat intake/g per person per day	Saturated fatty acids/%	Monounsaturated fatty acids/%	Polyunsaturated fatty acids/%
1970	121	19.3	15.9	4.3
1980	106	18.9	16.0	4.6
1990	86	16.7	15.3	6.7
2000	74	15.0	13.5	6.9

A huge number and variety of low-fat foods are currently available, though the labelling can be confusing. A product that is advertised as '90% fat-free' still contains 10% fat and '25% less fat' gives no indication of total fat present. Visible fats are obvious to the consumer and consumption can be lowered, by using less butter (or substituting low-fat spreads) on bread, cutting fat off meat and switching from frying to grilling food. However, invisible fats are harder to remove from the diet. Manufactured products (pies, burgers, cakes, biscuits, etc.) are often very high in fat, and nuts contain significant quantities too. In egg yolk and milk, the fat is hidden by being held in the liquid as an emulsion. The fat contents of a range of foods are listed in Table SP5.3.

Fat often enhances the flavour of foods – think about the taste of roast potatoes, chips (French fries), and potato crisps, compared with that of plain boiled potatoes. Dietary fats also contain the fat-soluble vitamins, A, D, E and K which are essential for good health, as will be described in SP9.

Fat is a very concentrated source of energy, providing more than twice as much energy per gram as the other energy sources, carbohydrate and protein. Thus a small amount of fat produces a lot of energy. This is important for people with a small appetite, people who are being artificially fed due to a medical condition, for athletes or others undertaking strenuous activity. However, it is very easy to consume too much energy inadvertently in the form of fat and this overconsumption can lead to obesity. Surplus fat is not removed from the body, but is stored in droplets in the cells of adipose (fat) tissue, beneath the skin and elsewhere. The human body appears to have an almost unlimited capacity to store fat. Some of the issues around obesity will be explored further in SP8 and the role of fat in coronary heart disease in SP14. Metabolic activities of the adipose tissue also play a role in maintaining the immune system and in controlling glucose levels in the blood. As mentioned above, lipids are also used to produce important cell components and signalling molecules.

Table SP5.3 Typical fat content of a range of foods, listed in descending order.

Food	Fat content/%
lard	100
butter	82
margarine	81
double cream	54
low-fat spread	38
cheddar cheese	34
smoked mackerel	31
chocolate	31
pork sausage	30
beefburger	24
beef (rump steak)	14
rich fruitcake	12
boiled egg	11
cheese and tomato pizza	10
deep-fried potato chips	6.7
roast chicken	5.4
smoked salmon	4.5
oven-baked chips	4.2
whole milk	3.9
rice	1.0
skimmed milk	0.2
potatoes (boiled)	0.1

Summary of SP5

1   Triacylglycerols are composed of glycerol with three fatty acid tails.

2   The fatty acids may be saturated, with no double bonds, or unsaturated, with one or more double bonds between the carbon atoms.

3   Fats containing saturated fatty acids have higher melting temperatures, since the molecules pack together more neatly than those with double bonds and therefore with bends in the tails.

4   Other lipids include phospholipids and cholesterol and substances derived from them, and lipoproteins.

5   Fats have a number of important functions in the body and since humans cannot synthesise some of the fatty acids, some fat is important in the diet.

6   Fats also contain fat-soluble vitamins.

7   Fats are energy-rich and excess in the diet is stored in adipose tissue, which can lead to obesity.

Answer to Activity SP5.1

Table SP5.4 Completed Table SP5.1. Names and properties of a selection of fatty acids.

Name of fatty acid	Source	No. of carbon atoms	Saturation	No. of carbon-to-carbon double bonds	Fatty acid 'family'
butyric	butter	4	saturated	0	
lauric	butter	12	saturated	0	
myristic	butter, nutmeg	14	saturated	0	
palmitic	oil palm, coconut palm	16	saturated	0	
stearic	butter, beef fat, lard and hard margarine	18	saturated	0	
arachidic	peanuts, butter	20	saturated	0	
oleic	olive oil, cod liver oil, etc.	18	monounsaturated	1	n-9 (omega 9)
linoleic	meat, eggs, nuts, oils	18	polyunsaturated	2	n-6 (omega 6)
(alpha) linolenic	green leafy vegetables, nuts, poultry meat	18	polyunsaturated	3	n-3 (omega 3)
arachidonic	plant oils, especially peanuts	20	polyunsaturated	4	n-6 (omega 6)
eicosapentaenoic (EPA)	oily fish	20	polyunsaturated	5	n-3 (omega 3)
docosahexaenoic (DHA)	oily fish	22	polyunsaturated	6	n-3 (omega 3)

Carbohydrates

6.1 Introduction

Carbohydrates are traditionally thought of as the major source of energy in the human diet. The amount and type of carbohydrate in the diet does, however, vary considerably, particularly between populations living in different parts of the world, as shown in Figure SP6.1.

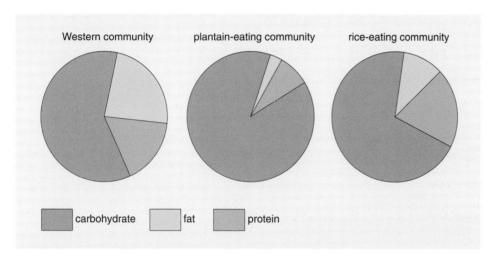

Figure SP6.1 Percentage intake of the macronutrients in three types of community characterised by different diets. Plantains are similar to bananas and are eaten in Latin America, the Caribbean and parts of Asia, though more as a cooked vegetable than a fruit.

Each of the circles divided into segments in Figure SP6.1 is called a pie chart. If you are not familiar with pie charts, you should now read the relevant section in the *Maths Skills Booklet*. The whole of each 'pie' represents 100% of the diet, and then the size of the coloured segments represents the percentage of carbohydrate, fat and protein in the various diets. Pie charts are useful for representing data where the precise values are less important than the comparison between the data.

● Which of the communities depicted in Figure SP6.1 eats the most carbohydrate in their diet? Which eats the most fat? Which eats the most protein?

◍ The plantain-eating community eats the most carbohydrate, since the biggest 'slice' of their 'pie' is the carbohydrate 'slice'. The Western community eats the most fat and the rice-eating community eats the most protein. The protein 'slice' of the rice-eating community 'pie' is just slightly larger than the protein 'slice' in the Western community 'pie'.

Activity SP6.1

What are the main sources of carbohydrate in your own diet? Use the information from the labels on food packets to draw up a table to compare the carbohydrate and sugar content of some of the foods that you eat regularly – try to choose at least 10 items. Decide how best to order the items in your table and label the columns clearly. (You might like to look back to Table SP5.3 as an example.)

Carbohydrate is a general term that includes various kinds of sugars, together with starch, cellulose and other related compounds.

● Remembering that 'hydro' means 'water', what elements would you expect to find in a molecule of 'carbohydrate'?

◐ Water contains the elements hydrogen and oxygen (H_2O) and 'carbo' is the first part of the name of the element carbon (symbol C), so you would expect carbohydrates to contain, carbon, hydrogen and oxygen – and they do!

6.2 Monosaccharides

The simplest sugars are called monosaccharides (pronounced 'mono-sack-a-rides'), meaning 'one-sugar'. Three of these are important in the human diet, namely glucose, fructose and galactose.

6.2.1 Glucose

Glucose (sometimes called dextrose) is an important building block in many other carbohydrates. It is a monosaccharide with the molecular formula $C_6H_{12}O_6$. However, there are very many different ways of drawing a molecule made up of six carbon, 12 hydrogen and six oxygen atoms, whilst still giving all the atoms the correct number of bonds and so it is necessary to have more than just its molecular formula to identify glucose.

● What is the formula called that shows how atoms are arranged in a molecule?

◐ It is called the structural formula (SP4.2).

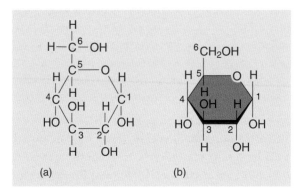

Figure SP6.2 (a) Structural formula of glucose. The carbon atoms are numbered for ease of reference. (b) Simplified structural formula of glucose.

● Look at the representation of the structural formula of a glucose molecule in Figure SP6.2a. How are the carbon atoms arranged?

◐ You should be able to see that the molecule includes a six-sided ring (hexagon), with a carbon atom (C) at five of the corners and an oxygen atom (O) at the sixth. The sixth carbon atom is located above the plane of the ring.

You might like to check that the structural formula of glucose in Figure SP6.2a agrees with the molecular formula $C_6H_{12}O_6$, i.e. that there are six carbon atoms, 12 hydrogen atoms and six oxygen atoms in the molecule.

● Now look at the carbon atoms in Figure SP6.2a numbered 1 to 4, which are part of the ring. What other atoms or groups are attached to each of them? And what are attached to carbon numbers 5 and 6?

◐ Carbon atoms 1, 2, 3 and 4 each have one H and one OH group attached. Sometimes the H points up above the ring and the OH points down (carbons 1, 2 and 4) and sometimes the OH points up and the H points down (carbon 3). Carbon atom 5 is also part of the ring and has an H pointing down, but is attached to carbon 6 pointing up. Carbon 6 is attached to two H atoms and an OH group.

Because this representation looks quite complex, the structural formula of glucose is often simplified, as here in Figure SP6.2b.

● What similarities and differences can you see between the formulae in Figures SP6.2a and b?

◐ Formula (b) looks less complicated because the carbon atoms around the ring have been omitted, though their numbers are still there. The plane of the ring has been shaded in to make it more obvious. The two hydrogen atoms attached to carbon 6 have been added together and written beside the carbon and before the OH, to give CH_2OH. The H and OH groups attached to carbons 1 to 4 remain unchanged, as does the oxygen in the ring.

You may also have noticed that there is some indication of the three-dimensional nature of the molecule, by making the bond between carbons 2 and 3 thicker, to indicate that this part of the ring is at the front. Then the bonds between carbons 2 and 1, and between carbons 3 and 4, taper from front to back, indicating that the ring part of the molecule is going away from the reader, so that carbon 5 and the oxygen atom in the ring are at the back. In fact, the ring is not a flat hexagon as shown here; the atoms around it form a zig-zag, but that complexity is omitted here.

Glucose is produced by plants in photosynthesis, by combining carbon dioxide from the air and water taken up by the roots, using light energy. It is found in, for example, grapes (7% by mass) and onions (2%), but the richest natural source is honey (31%). Blood contains about 80–100 mg of glucose in every 100 ml. Another way of measuring this is in units called millimoles, and the normal blood glucose range is 4–7 mmol per litre. This so-called 'blood sugar' level is closely controlled by hormones such as insulin.

● There are 1000 mg in 1 g and 1000 ml in 1 litre. If there are 80 mg of glucose in 100 ml blood, what is the concentration of glucose in blood in g per litre?

◐ 100 ml is one-tenth of a litre. So if there are 80 mg glucose in one-tenth of a litre, there will be 800 mg in a whole litre. There are 1000 mg in 1 g, so 800 mg is the same as 0.8 g. So the concentration of glucose in blood is 0.8 g in 1 litre, or 0.8 g per litre.

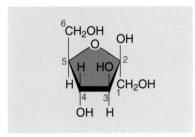

Figure SP6.3 The structural formula of fructose.

6.2.2 Fructose and galactose

Fructose and galactose are two more monosaccharides, similar to glucose. The following questions explore their structures.

Question SP6.1 Using the structural formula of glucose in Figure SP6.2 and that of fructose in Figure SP6.3, identify whether the following statements are true or false, giving your reason in each case.

(a) Both glucose and fructose contain a ring with five carbon atoms and one oxygen atom.

(b) Both glucose and fructose have the same molecular formula (number and types of atoms in the molecule). ◀

● The only difference between glucose and galactose is that galactose has the H atom on carbon 4 pointing down and the OH group sticking up above the plane of the ring. Based on Figure SP6.2b, sketch a galactose molecule.

◗ Check your answer against the structure given in Figure SP6.4 (p. 80).

Fructose, like glucose, is found naturally in honey (about 35%) and in some fruits and vegetables. Gram for gram, fructose is about twice as sweet as table sugar (sucrose, see SP6.3) and so only half as much is needed to sweeten foods. Fructose can be produced industrially from corn syrup and is now very common in many manufactured foods. Galactose does not occur naturally as a monosaccharide. All three monosaccharides are more commonly found combined together in pairs to form disaccharides.

6.3 Disaccharides

The most common pairings of monosaccharides to make disaccharides are:

glucose + fructose = sucrose
glucose + galactose = lactose
glucose + glucose   = maltose

● Recalling how amino acid monomers (Figure SP4.4) are linked to make proteins and how fatty acid monomers are linked to glycerol molecules in fats (Figure SP5.2), how are two monosaccharide monomers linked to make a disaccharide?

◗ They are linked by the removal of a molecule of water, as shown in Figure SP6.5. Because the linkage is between carbon atoms 1 and 4, this type of linkage is called a 1,4-glycosidic linkage.

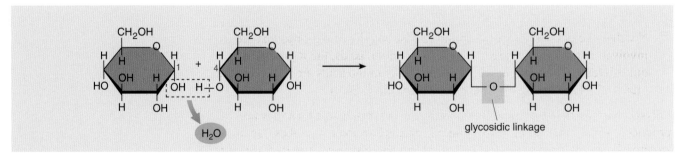

Figure SP6.5 Linkage of two monosaccharides, by a 1,4-glycosidic linkage, to form a disaccharide.

● Which two monosaccharides are being linked in Figure SP6.5? What is the name of the disaccharide formed?

◉ The two monosaccharides are both molecules of glucose and so the disaccharide is maltose.

Maltose is the sugar produced when starches are broken down in germinating grains, such as those of wheat or barley, to produce 'malt' for the production of beer. Maltose is also found in malted drinks (such as 'Horlicks') and biscuits. Sucrose is the white sugar normally bought for use in the home, extracted from sugar beet and sugar cane, and used in large quantities in manufactured foods. During the production of white sugar, golden syrup, brown sugar and molasses are also produced. Lactose is, as its name suggests, found in milk, both human, which contains 7% lactose, and that of other mammals (e.g. cows' milk contains up to 5% lactose).

6.4 Oligosaccharides

If another glucose molecule were placed alongside the disaccharide formed in Figure SP6.5, it would be possible to link that third glucose through another glycosidic linkage generating a chain of three monomer units and another molecule of water. This process could be continued to make a longer and longer chain. A molecule with more than two but less than about 10 monosaccharide monomer units is called an oligosaccharide. Oligosaccharides are synthesised in large quantities by certain plants that we use as food, such as peas and beans, onions, leeks and garlic. The oligosaccharides made by these particular plants often include some unusual monosaccharides and are not easily digested by human digestive enzymes. So they pass largely unchanged into the large intestine where the bacteria present ferment them, producing certain rather smelly compounds and some gases, which can cause flatulence.

6.5 Polysaccharides

Just as a series of amino acids can be linked together in a long chain to make a polypeptide, so a series of monosaccharides can be linked together via glycosidic linkages in a long chain to make a polysaccharide. Polysaccharides are made up of hundreds or up to tens of thousands of monosaccharide units, though in the most common polysaccharides, the monosaccharide monomers are all the same, namely glucose.

● Are the amino acids making up any one natural polypeptide chain all the same?

◉ No, they are not. Although the amino and carboxylic acid groups that are involved in the linkages are common to all amino acids, the R groups are quite diverse. The order in which the different amino acids are linked can be vital to the functioning of the completed protein (SP4.6).

Polysaccharides have two main functions in the organisms in which they are produced; some, such as cellulose (found in plants and some microbes), act as structural materials, while others, such as starch and glycogen, are used as a way of storing carbohydrates.

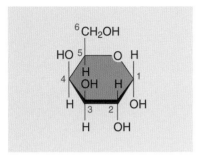

Figure SP6.4 The structural formula of galactose.

6.5.1 Cellulose

It is conventional to use 'powers of ten' notation when writing very large numbers. If you are not familiar with this, now is the time to read the appropriate section of the *Maths Skills Booklet*.

The most abundant large molecule made by living organisms is cellulose. 10^{15} kg of cellulose are synthesised and degraded on Earth each year.

● There are 1000 kg in 1 tonne. How many tonnes of cellulose are synthesised and degraded on Earth each year? Write the answer out as an ordinary number and in words.

◗ 10^{15} kg is equivalent to 10^{12} tonnes, which would be written as 1 000 000 000 000.

Cellulose is so common because it forms the structural framework of the walls of all plant cells. Each cellulose molecule is a polymer composed of an unbranched chain of at least 500 glucose monomers. These chains can pack side by side to give a very tough fibre, which is strengthened by large numbers of hydrogen bonds between adjacent chains (Figure SP6.6). Cotton is almost pure cellulose, so you can assess for yourself the strength of the fibres and the hydrogen bonds, by stretching a thread of cotton until it breaks.

● Look back to SP4.6.1 to recall the atoms that can be involved in hydrogen bonds. Using Figure SP6.5, identify the atoms in cellulose which are likely to be involved in this sort of bonding.

◗ Hydrogen bonds can involve nitrogen atoms, but none of these occur in a glucose polymer such as cellulose, so here we are only concerned with bonding between a hydrogen atom attached to an oxygen atom (OH group) and an oxygen atom elsewhere. Since each glucose monomer has several OH groups, several hydrogen bonds can form between adjacent chains (Figure 6.6a).

Figure SP6.6 (a) Simplified diagram of part of three cellulose molecules, showing hydrogen bonds (dotted lines) between the glucose monomers in the polysaccharide chains. (b) Cellulose fibres in hemp.

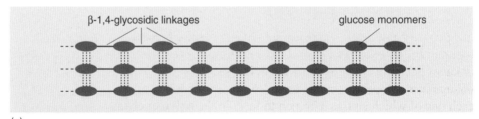

(a)

(b)

50 μm

Animal cells are unable to synthesise the enzymes that break down the particular linkage between the glucose molecules in cellulose (called a β-1,4-glycosidic linkage, where β is the Greek letter 'beta'), and so cellulose is an indigestible component of the human diet. Herbivorous animals, such as horses, cows and rabbits, which live only on plant material, harbour huge colonies of microbes in their guts which do have the ability to produce the appropriate enzyme, so enabling them to release the glucose units for their nutrition. Cellulose and some other less common polysaccharides that are indigestible in humans are called 'dietary fibre' or, more correctly, since they are not all fibrous, 'non-starch polysaccharides' or NSPs (see SP6.5.4), to distinguish them from starch, which can be digested.

6.5.2 Starch

Both plants and animals need a way of storing glucose, since this is an important source of energy. In animals, glucose is stored as an insoluble polymer called glycogen; we will start with the glucose storage polymer in plants, which is starch.

● What is the value to the plant (in the wild) of storing starch in (a) potatoes and (b) grains of wheat or corn?

◔ (a) Potatoes are formed at the end of one growing season of the potato plant. If left in the ground, as they would be in the wild, each potato can grow quickly at the start of the next season, into several new plants, breaking down the starch into glucose to provide energy and materials for the new growth. (b) In wheat or corn (maize), the starch similarly provides food for the germinating grain when it begins to grow the following season.

Starch is composed mostly of a polysaccharide called amylopectin, which contains at least several hundred glucose monomers. In amylopectin, the glucose monomers are linked in a different way from the links in cellulose. The so-called α-1,4-glycosidic linkages (where α is the Greek letter 'alpha') in starch can be digested by enzymes in the human digestive system, to release the glucose monomers, whereas the β-1,4-glycosidic linkages found in cellulose cannot. (The difference between α and β linkages need not concern you.) There is a second type of linkage in amylopectin (called an α-1,6-glycosidic linkage) each one of which causes a branch to form in the polymer chain (Figure SP6.7). Starch also contains similar molecules with α-1,4-glycosidic linkages, but no branches, called amylose.

A consequence of the branching in amylopectin is that adjacent chains of glucose monomers in starch cannot pack closely enough for large numbers of hydrogen bonds to form to hold the polymer molecules together, as happens in the straight-chain molecules of cellulose. So starch cannot have a support function. Some hydrogen bonds do form between adjacent amylose chains and between the unbranched parts of the amylopectin chains and this bonding makes starch grains in some plants quite hard. For that reason, starchy foods are often processed before we eat them, for example, wheat is ground to make flour, for bread,

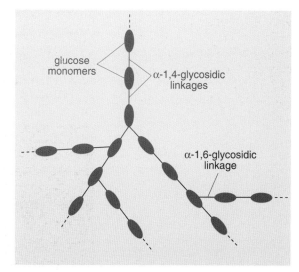

Figure SP6.7 Simplified diagram of amylopectin, the main component of starch, showing the branched structure.

81

cakes, etc. and starchy grains are treated in various ways to make breakfast cereals. This processing disrupts the hard starch grains and makes the amylopectin and amylose more accessible to digestive enzymes.

Cooking starch has the same effect. Consider what happens when we thicken sauces with cornflour, which is starch obtained from maize seeds. Cold water cannot penetrate the individual grains and so starch can be mixed evenly with water at low temperatures. However, when it is heated to above about 50 °C, molecules of water can get amongst the amylose and amylopectin chains and bond to them with hydrogen bonds. The starch grains swell and begin to soften. Some types of starch grain can absorb up to 25 times their own mass of water, corresponding to about 400 water molecules per molecule of starch. As the swelling continues, the starch grains merge and the shorter amylose chains emerge from the grains and get tangled up with each other and with the amylopectin chains, giving a three-dimensional network, held together by hydrogen bonds. These processes thicken sauces made with cornflour. Continued stirring breaks some of the hydrogen bonds and the sauce may become thinner again, but when it is cooled, the hydrogen bonding re-forms, as when custard or blancmange sets.

Lumps appear in a sauce if the starch grains are not fully dispersed before it is heated. If starch is added directly to hot water, the outer layers of the starch grain absorb water very rapidly, forming a barrier that prevents water reaching the centre and so lumps of starch remain. This outcome can be prevented by mixing the cornflour with a little cold water before it is added to hot water. The alternative way to make a sauce involves making a 'roux', in which the flour is mixed with melted butter before the liquid is added. This fat covers the starch grains, effectively 'waterproofing' them so that they can be dispersed before they absorb much liquid, which gives a much more controlled thickening.

6.5.3 Glycogen

The glucose-storage molecule in animals, which is equivalent to starch in plants, is called glycogen. It is stored in human liver and muscle. Like amylopectin, glycogen is composed of glucose monomers, but it has a much more branched structure, with very many short branches and so it is associated with much more water, held amongst the chains by hydrogen bonds. Although important as a short-term glucose store in humans, we do not consume a significant amount of glycogen in our diet.

● Based on the information you have just read, which foods that we eat might contain glycogen?

◑ If glycogen is found in human liver and muscle, it is reasonable to assume that it would be found in the same parts of other animals. So, any meat (muscle) and liver in our diet are likely to contain glycogen.

6.5.4 Non-starch polysaccharides (NSPs)

Dietary fibre, also called roughage, is the part of the diet that cannot be digested by the enzymes in the human gut. Scientifically it is referred to as the non-starch polysaccharide (NSP) component of the diet. Cellulose (SP6.5.1) is the main source of dietary fibre and because it does not dissolve in water, it is known as insoluble NSP. The two other types of NSP are soluble in water – pectins from fruits and mucilages from pulses and oats, which form jelly-like structures in water.

Both insoluble and soluble NSP are thought to be important to a healthy diet. Diets that contain plentiful insoluble fibre result in bulkier gut contents, since the fibre absorbs water. Because gut muscle activity is stimulated by the larger volume, such bulky food travels more quickly through the digestive system. For example, a meal high in NSPs might take less than a day to pass through the gut, while a meal low in NSPs might take several days or longer. In fact, NSP foods can be used as 'bulk purgatives' to loosen the bowel in cases of constipation.

A shorter transit time in the gut reduces the amount of contact between intestinal tissue and any potentially harmful substances, for example, cancer-causing molecules, in the diet. Fibre may also actually bind to potentially toxic substances and hence aid their elimination via defaecation. For this reason, it is thought that diets high in insoluble fibre are protective against conditions such as bowel cancer, and indeed, the incidence of bowel cancer is lower in populations with a higher intake of insoluble fibre. Soluble fibre, such as that found in peas, beans, lentils and oats, seems to be useful in helping control some types of diabetes by slowing down the absorption of sugars into the blood. Diets high in fibre are also associated with a lower incidence of coronary heart disease and as they also tend to be low in fat and sugar, and in some cases have higher levels of some vitamins, there may be further beneficial effects.

Bulky food also reduces the need for straining at defaecation, which can cause piles or haemorrhoids (dilated veins causing painful swelling at the anus). Diets containing high levels of insoluble fibre have also been reported to have a protective effect against some other gastrointestinal disorders, including formation of gallstones (small stone-like structures formed in the gall bladder), appendicitis (inflammation of the appendix) and diverticular disease. In diverticular disease areas of the gut wall bulge out to form 'pockets' (or diverticula). They are thought to form when the walls of the intestine are pushing against hard and compacted gut contents, such as those which can occur in a diet low in fibre. Gut contents become stuck in these pockets, infection can occur and the gut can become painful and inflamed.

There is also evidence that increasing the NSP content of the diet, without increasing the energy content, results in a weight loss of about 0.5 kg per month. The exact mechanisms that cause this are not yet clear but an increase in wholegrain cereals and in fruit and vegetables in the diet can make a useful contribution to weight control.

6.6   Carbohydrate digestion

Question SP6.2 Before considering how carbohydrates can be digested, it would be useful to make yourself a summary table of the main carbohydrates (monosaccharides, disaccharides and polysaccharides) in the diet and their relationship to each other. Compare yours with the version given in the answer. ◀

Digestion breaks down both polysaccharides and disaccharides into monosaccharides, which are small enough to be absorbed into the bloodstream.

● Which polysaccharide cannot be digested by humans?

● Cellulose cannot be digested; the main polysaccharide that undergoes digestion is starch.

The digestion of starch takes place in several stages. An enzyme in the saliva, called salivary amylase, begins the process, breaking starch into shorter-chain polysaccharides. It is not clear if the overall digestion of starchy foods is affected by whether someone chews each mouthful of their food well or eats quickly with minimal chewing. The stomach does not produce any more starch-digesting enzymes, although the salivary amylase may continue to function for some time there. When the food reaches the small intestine, a second amylase is secreted by the pancreas. This pancreatic amylase breaks down polysaccharides into short chains of monosaccharide units, called dextrins, and disaccharides. Digestion of all the carbohydrates into their component monosaccharides, is completed by a series of enzymes secreted by cells in the lining of the wall of the small intestine.

Question SP6.3 Remembering that enzymes are usually, but not always, named by using -ase to replace the ending of the substance being digested, complete Table SP6.1 to show the final stages of carbohydrate digestion. ◀

Table SP6.1 Carbohydrate digestion in the small intestine.

Enzyme	Substance being digested	Products of digestion
dextrinase		
	lactose	
maltase		
		glucose and fructose

● In the majority of the world's population, the production of the enzyme lactase starts to fall after weaning, and continues to decline during childhood and adolescence so that adults produce no lactase. Why is lactase more important in young children?

◔ Lactase is the enzyme that digests lactose, the sugar found in milk. In babies, where milk is the only source of their nutrients, digesting lactose is essential to provide glucose.

In fact, most Northern Europeans, and their descendants in other parts of the world, retain their ability to produce lactase, and therefore to digest lactose in milk, throughout life. In many other population groups, lactase is absent in adults. For example, it is estimated that 80–95% of adult African and Oriental people produce no lactase. If they consume milk, the lactose is not digested and remains in the intestine, increasing the population of those gut bacteria that use lactose as a food source, and resulting in severe abdominal pain and watery diarrhoea. This extreme reaction is triggered even by small amounts of milk and is known as lactose intolerance. Milk products in which lactose is converted into other molecules, such as lactic acid in yoghurt, can safely be consumed by individuals with lactose intolerance.

6.7 Absorption of carbohydrates

Once carbohydrates have been digested completely, the monosaccharides (mainly glucose) are absorbed into the cells of the small intestine, from where they pass into the bloodstream and are thus distributed to all parts of the body. Since cells, and particularly brain cells, work best with a constant supply of glucose as a source of energy for metabolism, if glucose were simply transported throughout the body after absorption and used as required, there would be a serious problem.

● Can you think what this would be?

◐ There would be a shortage of glucose between meals, which would result in blood glucose levels sometimes being very low, for example overnight, and during and after strenuous exercise.

So the levels of glucose must be regulated so that they do not fall seriously between meals or rise excessively when a meal has been eaten and glucose is being absorbed from the gut into the bloodstream. In an individual who has not eaten for several hours, the blood glucose level will be typically in the range 80–100 mg per 100 ml (4–7 mmol per litre) of blood. After a meal, this level rises, but rarely to more than 140 mg per 100 ml (11 mmol per litre) blood, even if large amounts of carbohydrate have been eaten. And then blood glucose levels return to their typical values within about two and a half hours after a meal, even though absorption from the gut is continuing. The level of glucose is controlled largely by two hormones that are secreted into the bloodstream from the pancreas. Insulin reduces the blood glucose levels when the levels rise following digestion of a meal, and glucagon causes glucose levels to rise again between meals. In simple terms, these effects are achieved by moving glucose in and out of storage.

● What is the glucose storage molecule in animals called?

◐ The molecule is glycogen (SP6.5.3).

Glycogen is stored in the liver and muscles, though it is mostly liver glycogen that is used as the temporary store to and from which glucose can be shuttled to regulate blood sugar levels. Glycogen in muscles is mostly used to provide energy for muscle contraction. Failure to produce sufficient insulin, or failure of cells to respond appropriately to insulin, leads to the condition known as diabetes, in which too much glucose remains in the blood, with serious consequences for health. The amount of glycogen that can be stored is quite limited (no more than a few hundred grams in total), so the stores are filled quite quickly and if more glucose is available, then the excess could be converted into fat for storage. Fat stores in the body are effectively unlimited. However, it appears that excess carbohydrate is normally used for energy rather than being converted to fat.

Activity SP6.2

Look back at the summary of protein digestion and absorption that you produced as your answer to Activity SP4.1. With that experience, now is the time to try another one, this time for the digestion and absorption of carbohydrate. When you have completed your summary, compare it with the one at the end of this study period.

6.8   Glycaemic index (GI)

Different sorts of food have different effects on the blood glucose level, related to the speed at which glucose from them is released during digestion and taken up into the bloodstream. The measure of how much glucose appears in the blood after standard doses of foods in a given time is known as the glycaemic index (GI). Glucose is given a GI value of 100 and other foods are ranked relative to it. Foods with a high GI (above 85) produce a lot of glucose into the blood quite quickly, e.g. highly processed and sugary breakfast cereals, bananas and white bread. Those with low GI values (below 60), e.g. porridge, muesli, apples, beans and pasta are digested and absorbed more slowly and so produce a more gradual rise in blood glucose. The GI value is partly dependent on the type of carbohydrate in the food. For example, starch can be classified into rapidly digestible starch, slowly digestible starch and resistant starch. Resistant starch is found in foods such as unripe bananas and in raw potatoes. It can only be digested if the foods are cooked, otherwise it passes undigested out of the body in the faeces. Relatively unprocessed breakfast wholegrain cereals, such as porridge oats and muesli, contain more slowly digestible starch and so take longer to be digested than the processed alternatives. They therefore produce a smaller and less dramatic rise in blood glucose level after eating. A similar comparison can be made between pasta, with 43% slowly digestible starch, and white bread with only 4% slowly digestible starch. GI values also appear to be affected by the other food components (fat, protein, etc.) present in the food or in the whole meal. A diet containing low GI foods can help weight control as the foods are digested more slowly and so produce a feeling of satiety for longer. Low GI foods are important for people with diabetes since they release glucose into the blood at a steadier rate and they are important in the nutrition of athletes too, as you will see in SP16.

6.9   Carbohydrate requirements

It is much less easy to determine the amount of carbohydrate needed per day than it is for protein and fat, but to maintain a steady weight, the average adult probably needs a minimum of about 150 g per day. If the level falls lower, then glucose, essential for the cells of the brain and nervous system, has to be provided from the stored glycogen. Once the glycogen stores have been exhausted, the body can convert the glycerol part of fat molecules, and the carbon-containing part of some of the amino acids, from proteins, into glucose.

6.10 Carbohydrates and health

Since carbohydrates are such a varied group of molecules, it is not surprising that there are numerous links with health, and that some are beneficial and some detrimental.

● Three links with health have already been mentioned. Identify them and any other links of which you are aware.

◉ SP6.5.4 mentioned the beneficial effects of NSPs on the functioning of the digestive system.

SP6.6 described lactose intolerance, in some populations, where adults are unable to digest the sugar, lactose, found in milk.

SP6.7 mentioned diabetes in which the control of the blood glucose level is faulty.

Other links you may have thought of are with obesity and with tooth decay.

There is no clear link between the intake of either starch or sugar and obesity. As mentioned earlier (SP6.7), carbohydrates are not normally converted to fat. However, in a diet containing large amounts of both, the carbohydrate is used to provide most of the energy requirements, leaving the fat to be stored, leading to obesity. If less carbohydrate is consumed, more of the dietary fat is used as an energy source. Overweight individuals are more likely to develop diabetes, though again, there is no direct link with carbohydrate consumption.

The link between tooth decay (dental caries) and the intake of sugary foods is much clearer. Carbohydrates present in the mouth serve as an ideal source of nutrients for the bacteria that normally live there, in the moist film of saliva covering the teeth. These bacteria, which form a layer called plaque, produce lactic acid and enzymes that digest proteins. The plaque can keep the acid in contact with the tooth surface for up to two hours before it is neutralised by the saliva. Over time, the acid gradually dissolves the calcium salts in the tooth enamel, and the enamel protein is destroyed by the bacterial enzymes. Despite the resistance of the enamel, eventually the surface is breached and the underlying softer dentine is dissolved and cavities form in the teeth. The problem is made worse by eating frequent meals and in particular by 'snacking' on sugary items between meals. Sorbitol, mannitol and xylitol are unusual monosaccharides, known as polyols or sugar alcohols. They taste sweet but cannot be used by the bacteria in the mouth and are therefore used in sugar-free chewing gum.

● What was one effect of eating 'unusual monosaccharides'? You may need to check back to SP6.4.

● They cannot be digested by the normal enzymes, so they pass through to the colon, where they are fermented by the gut bacteria, leading to flatulence. This occurs with sorbitol and other polyols too.

Writing accounts: The following activity asks you to write an account of 250–300 words. Many people find writing an account like this quite daunting. They report that they 'know what to say, but can't put it into words', so if you feel like that, take heart; you are not alone! You should tackle a task like this in two parts. First of all re-read the sections in which you recall reading the relevant information. If you have been making brief notes, or highlighting relevant words as you go along, finding the information you need should be relatively straightforward. Note down the important points, which may only be a few crucial words, to remind you of the sorts of things you will need to include in the account. Then start to plan how to structure the account. You may be able to do this planning in your head, or you may need to jot some points down on paper. Decide where to start, and then what sequence you will follow. Several points on the same subject should be grouped together into paragraphs. Then try writing the first draft of your answer. Since you are using your own notes, you will automatically be expressing the points in your own words. The phrase 'in your own words' here simply means 'do not copy whole sentences or even phrases directly from someone else's writing'. The reason for this instruction is so that the reader of your account knows that you understand the topic you are writing about, and that you have not just copied someone else's words without having any understanding of the subject. The advice about the number of words is to give you a rough indication of the amount of detail you are expected to include in your answer. You should aim to be within about 10% of the word count given. So here, if your first draft is less than about 225 words, you have probably not included everything. If it is more than 330 words, you may have included information which was not strictly necessary, or perhaps you have not expressed your information in the most concise way, or have said the same thing twice. So, count the words in the first version of your answer and read the whole thing through again, to see what changes are necessary. Most writers find they need several drafts before they are happy with their material. You might find it useful to read the account out loud to someone else, and ask them if they understand it. Once it makes sense and the word count is about right, then it is probably good enough. If there is a version written for you, as here, then compare your answer with that. But remember that there are many ways of expressing the same points and your version is probably at least as good, if not better, than the 'official' one.

Activity SP6.3

In your own words, write an account of about 250–300 words, in which you explain the benefits of eating a bowl of porridge, with sliced apple, for breakfast, rather than a bowl of sweetened processed breakfast cereal.

Activity SP6.4

Now that you have completed SP4–6, on the macronutrients in the diet, it would be a good opportunity to look through the articles on nutrition that you were advised to start collecting in Activity SP1.1 and re-read those that are relevant to proteins, fats and carbohydrates. You should now be better equipped to understand some of the scientific terminology used and also to make some judgements on the accuracy or otherwise of the statements in the articles.

Summary of SP6

1   Carbohydrates are composed of monosaccharides, such as glucose, fructose and galactose.

2   Monosaccharides can be linked in pairs to form disaccharides, like sucrose (table sugar).

3   Linkage of larger numbers of monosaccharides forms polysaccharides, such as starch in plants and glycogen in animals.

4   Cellulose is the most common polysaccharide, but because of the way that the glucose units are linked, it cannot be digested by humans.

5   Other carbohydrates are broken down during digestion to their component monosaccharides, in particular to glucose which is an important source of energy for cells.

6   The glycaemic index (GI) of foods is a measure of how fast glucose appears in the blood after the food is eaten.

7   There are numerous links between carbohydrates and impaired health, including tooth decay and diabetes.

Answer to Activity SP6.1

Table SP6.2 gives a possible list of carbohydrate sources. On the food labels, the values were given as grams (g) of carbohydrate and g of sugar per 100 g of the food, which is the same as %, so the columns have been labelled accordingly. The values have been given in decreasing order of carbohydrate content.

Table SP6.2 Typical carbohydrate and sugar content of a range of foods, listed in descending order of carbohydrate.

Food	Carbohydrates/%	Sugars/%
breakfast cereal	77	21
pasta (dry)	73	3
flour	70	1.5
digestive biscuits	68	20
strawberry jam	65	60
rice	57	trace
bread	48	4
potatoes	17	0.5
frozen peas	10	2
pasta sauce	6	5

Answer to Activity SP6.2

Figure SP6.8 shows one possible way of presenting the information.

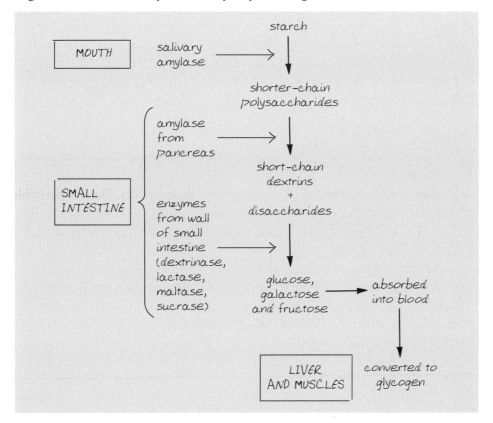

Figure SP6.8 Summary of the digestion and absorption of carbohydrate.

Answer to Activity SP6.3

Sweetened processed breakfast cereals are likely to contain more rapidly digestible starch than slowly digestible starch, together with sugar, usually sucrose. The cereal is a high GI food. Once eaten, the cereal therefore provides an immediate boost to blood glucose levels (which may make the person feel more wide-awake and ready to face the day). However, after this rapid and high boost to the blood glucose levels, all the starch and sugar has been digested and no more glucose is released into the blood. So the person may feel hungry again quite soon. Additionally, some of the sugar on the cereal remains on the teeth and increases the risk of dental caries, since the bacteria in the mouth convert it to acid, which attacks the tooth enamel.

Porridge and apple, on the other hand, are low GI foods containing a majority of slowly digestible starch and very little immediately available sugar. So the risk of dental caries is significantly reduced. The porridge and apple are digested more slowly when they reach the small intestine than the processed breakfast cereal would be. Thus there is no instant rise in blood glucose level, but a steadier and more prolonged appearance of glucose in the bloodstream, causing the person to feel satiated for longer. The person who eats porridge for breakfast is less likely to need to eat a snack before lunch. Not eating between meals (as well as lowering total food intake) may help with weight control.

(244 words)

Energy needs

7.1 Introduction

The human body needs energy not just for those things we think of as being 'energetic' – walking, sporting activities, etc. – but also for all those activities that go on unnoticed by us within our bodies.

● Try to think of five energy-requiring internal activities in the body.

● You might have thought of some of the following: breathing; heart beating; producing enzymes to digest food; moving food along the gut; producing urine; hair growth; nail growth; eye focusing and movement; thinking; healing accidental damage; replacing red blood cells; etc.

The rate at which energy is used by the body is called the metabolic rate. Even a person who is resting needs a significant amount of energy for all their internal processes.

7.2 Measuring the energy of foods

The energy content of food can be determined in the laboratory by using a piece of apparatus called a 'bomb calorimeter'. This consists of a metal container filled with oxygen in which a known amount of food is suspended. The food is heated electrically and burns with a small explosion (hence the term 'bomb'!). By surrounding the container with a known quantity of water, and carefully measuring its temperature rise, the amount of heat generated by the food can be calculated. This amount of heat released by burning the food in oxygen is equivalent to the energy released in the body when the food is completely broken down. This technique can be used for 'pure' proteins, fats and carbohydrates, giving the average energy yields listed in Table SP 7.1.

Table SP7.1 The energy yields of different nutrients.

Nutrient type	Available energy	
	/kcal per gram	/kJ per gram
protein	4	
fat	9	
carbohydrate	4	
alcohol	7	

Units of energy: One calorie is defined as the amount of heat (energy) needed to raise the temperature of one gram (1 g) of water by one degree Celsius (1 °C). This unit is rather small. To boil 500 g (half a litre) of water (i.e. to raise its temperature from cold to its boiling temperature of 100 °C) requires around 45 000 calories. So the more common unit is the kilocalorie, abbreviated to kcal, which is equal to 1000 calories. Kilocalories are also sometimes, and rather confusingly, referred to as Calories, with a capital C. The correct SI unit of energy is the joule (J), which again is rather small, and so the more common unit is the kilojoule (kJ). Kilocalories and kilojoules are easily converted since 1 kcal is equal to 4.2 kJ. Note that when you write a number with its units, you should always leave a space between the numerical value and the unit.

● Calculate the energy values of each of the nutrients in Table SP7.1 in kilojoules. Round your answers to the nearest whole number of kilojoules.

◐ The calculations are as follows:

protein: 4 kcal per gram = 4 × 4.2 kJ per gram = 16.8 kJ per gram

= 17 kJ per gram (to the nearest kJ)

fat: 9 kcal per gram = 9 × 4.2 kJ per gram = 37.8 kJ per gram

= 38 kJ per gram (to the nearest kJ)

carbohydrate: 4 kcal per gram = 4 × 4.2 kJ per gram = 16.8 kJ per gram

= 17 kJ per gram (to the nearest kJ)

alcohol: 7 kcal per gram = 7 × 4.2 kJ per gram = 29.4 kJ per gram

= 29 kJ per gram (to the nearest kJ)

Write these values into Table SP7.1 to complete the final column.

Question SP7.1 The nutritional information on a 150 g pot of low-fat yoghurt states that the pot provides 156 kcal.

(a) How many kilocalories does 100 g of the product provide? Try to work out a rough answer in your head, then confirm with a calculator.

(b) How many kilojoules per gram does the yoghurt contain, to the nearest kJ. ◀

Question SP7.2 The pot of yoghurt mentioned in Question SP7.1 contained 6.3 g protein, 26.1 g carbohydrate and 2.9 g fat. Confirm that it would produce 156 kcal when the yoghurt was completely digested. ◀

Question SP7.3 A miniature bottle of gin contains 50 ml and the gin weighs about 50 g. 40% of the gin is alcohol. Assuming that the gin is drunk with 200 ml of tonic, which provides 198 kJ, how does the total intake of kJ in the drink compare with that of eating the yoghurt in Question SP7.1? ◀

7.3 Measuring energy intake and output

Accurately measuring a person's energy intake should be relatively straightforward. It ought to be possible to identify all the foods that they eat and using values such as those in Table SP7.1, to calculate the total energy content. In practice, collecting the basic data is not so easy, for various reasons. For example, foods are variable in composition, both in the nutrients and in the amount of water they contain, and their energy content can be affected by the way that they are cooked. Additionally, individuals tend to under-report the amount of food that they consume. The estimated average requirements throughout life are given in Table SP7.2.

Table SP7.2 Dietary reference values (estimated average requirements, EAR) for energy through the human lifespan. Also shown are the extra (+) amounts of energy required during pregnancy and lactation.

Age	EAR / kcal per day	
	Males	Females
0–3 months	545	515
4–6 months	690	645
7–9 months	825	765
10–12 months	920	865
1–3 years	1230	1165
4–6 years	1715	1545
7–10 years	1970	1740
11–14 years	2220	1845
15–18 years	2755	2110
19–50 years	2550	1940
51–59 years	2550	1900
60–64 years	2380	1900
65–74 years	2330	1900
over 75 years	2100	1810
pregnancy		+200*
lactation		+450–480

* During the last three months (trimester).

Measuring someone's energy output is even less straightforward. If they are sitting still, then the only energy output is in the form of heat. So, the output can be measured by putting the person in a special sealed room in which their heat output can be measured. Alternatively, the energy used can be estimated by measuring the amount of oxygen they breathe in and the amount of carbon dioxide they give out, and there are also methods using radioactive isotopes. Under most circumstances, measuring energy output is an academic exercise, since appetite controls food intake and if body mass is constant, then energy input in food must equal energy output. However, in hospital patients who are receiving treatment that may affect their metabolism, or who are being fed intravenously, so that appetite cannot be a regulator, it is crucial to know that they are not being seriously overfed or underfed.

7.4 Factors affecting energy output

7.4.1 Basal metabolic rate (BMR)

In SP7.1, we mentioned that a significant amount of energy is needed for internal processes even when a person is resting. The basal metabolic rate (BMR) is the energy used in a given time by a person who is resting at a comfortable temperature and who has not eaten for the previous 12 hours.

● How might the metabolic rate be affected if the person (a) was in cold surroundings and (b) had just eaten a large meal?

◐ (a) A person in cold surroundings would probably be undertaking some additional activity trying to keep warm – for example, by rubbing the hands together or stamping the feet, putting on extra clothes, etc. Additionally, they might shiver. All these activities use additional energy and so would push the metabolic rate somewhat higher than its basal level.

(b) If the person had just eaten a large meal, additional energy would be expended in digesting that food. More digestive enzymes would need to be released and movements of the muscles in the gut wall would be increased to push the food along. Typically, about 10% of the energy intake of a meal is used in the processes of digesting it.

A typical BMR value is about 60 kcal (252 kJ) per hour for men, slightly less for women.

● In deep sleep, a person's metabolic rate might be 5–10 % lower than their BMR. This is called the minimal metabolic rate. What would a typical range of values be for the minimal metabolic rate for men?

◐ You can work this out either by calculating 5% and 10% of 60 kcal per hour and subtracting those values from the 60 kcal per hour to give the minimal metabolic rate for men. Or you could work out 90% and 95% of 60 kcal per hour to obtain the value directly. Using the first method,

$$5\% \text{ of } 60 \text{ kcal per hour} = \frac{5}{100} \times 60 \text{ kcal per hour} = 3 \text{ kcal per hour and}$$

similarly, 10% of 60 kcal = 6 kcal.

So, subtracting these values from 60 kcal per hour, gives a range of values for the minimal metabolic rate for men of between 54 and 57 kcal per hour (227–239 kJ per hour).

The precise value of the BMR for an individual is affected by a number of factors. The first, which has already been mentioned, is gender. Women have a slightly lower metabolic rate than men simply because the average female body has about 10% more fat than a male body of a similar weight. Adipose tissue (fat) consumes much less energy than a similar mass of muscle and other body tissues. So, the higher the proportion of fat, the lower the metabolic rate of that individual. The second factor affecting BMR is body mass. A larger body needs more energy to sustain it and so the BMR of a heavier person is higher. How much higher depends on whether the additional weight is made up of mostly muscle, as in a highly trained athlete, which consumes a lot of energy, or mostly fat, as in a person who is simply overweight, which consumes rather less.

During pregnancy and lactation, a woman's metabolic rate rises as her body is required to nourish the growing offspring. Babies have the highest metabolic rate, when measured per kg of body weight, and the BMR declines after that. This change is partly because the maturing body contains relatively less muscle tissue and relatively more fat. The failure to appreciate this gradual change and therefore the necessity for less food, may be a reason why many people put on weight in their later years. Various disease conditions, such as under- or overactivity of the thyroid gland, together with some drugs, and stress, can also affect BMR.

7.4.2 Physical activity

The level of physical activity that a person undertakes has a major effect on the amount of energy used, and it is, of course, the only aspect that is under voluntary control on a daily basis. The amount of energy expended in a particular activity has been shown by careful measurements to be related to a person's weight and therefore to their BMR. So for each type of exercise, it is possible to calculate the factor by which it increases the BMR. These factors are called metabolic equivalents (MET values) or sometimes physical activity ratios (PAR values) or physical activity levels (PAL values) (see SP15.3).

METs are commonly displayed on fitness machines in gyms. Brisk walking has a MET value of about 4, that is, the energy used is about 4 times greater than the energy used when sitting still. Swimming has a MET value of about 7, jogging at 10 km per hour has a MET value of 8, and playing squash can have a MET value of 12. Since the BMR for an individual can be read from tables based on age, gender and body mass (weight), METs provide a useful way to compare the effect of different sorts of exercise.

Summary of SP7

1   The energy of foods is measured in kilojoules (kJ) or in kilocalories (kcal).
2   The amount of energy used by a person awake but at rest, at a comfortable temperature, after fasting for 12 hours, is called the basal metabolic rate (BMR).
3   BMR differs with gender and changes with age and weight.
4   Physical activity uses more energy and so it increases the metabolic rate.

Energy balance

8.1 Introduction

When a person's energy intake and their energy output are equal, their body mass will remain stable. Scientifically speaking, we should always talk about body mass, rather than weight. However, since 'weight' is in common usage, and we talk about people being 'overweight', rather than 'overmass', the terms will be used interchangeably here.

8.2 The obesity epidemic

It is interesting to observe that many adults remain the same weight for years, even decades, despite professing to 'eat what they like', while others apparently spend much of their life 'on a diet' and yet remain overweight. Unfortunately, there is no secret to the 'success' of the first group and the 'failure' of the second. With a very few exceptions, it simply depends on a balance or imbalance in the energy intake, from food, and the energy output, in the activities that go on inside the body as well as voluntary physical activity. Children, of course, need a slightly higher intake than output to permit normal growth, and groups such as athletes with a very high output of energy, need a corresponding high energy input of food to maintain a stable weight.

However, the health of many adults and children at the start of the 21st century is being put at risk because they are overweight, or obese, largely as a result of taking in, over an extended period of time, more energy in the form of food than they use in activity. Over the past 50 years, lifestyles in the UK and other developed countries, have changed in ways that tend to promote obesity.

Question SP8.1 Make two lists of lifestyle changes in the UK, one related to food and one to activity, that have occurred over the last 50 years and which are likely to have contributed to 'the obesity epidemic'. Aim for at least four items on each list. ◀

Although some of the lifestyle changes apply specifically to adults, many affect children too. Children now spend much of their leisure time sitting watching TV, playing computer games, etc. and less time playing physical games outside. These habits develop partly from the attraction of the electronic world, but also because of parental concerns over their children's safety if they are playing outside. The marketing of high-energy snacks is often aimed at children; such snacks are easily available and can be consumed without breaking off from the latest DVD or computer game. Few children now walk to school, for reasons of both time, of their parents or carers, and safety.

So, maybe the obesity epidemic is not so surprising after all. Various UK Government initiatives are now in place to address the obesity problem.

8.2.1 Measuring obesity

Obesity is defined as a greatly elevated body weight above the desirable level, to an extent that there is a seriously increased risk to health. Numerically, it is based on the calculation of a person's body mass index (BMI).

● Check back to SP1.5 to find the formula for calculating BMI.

● The formula is $BMI = \dfrac{\text{weight in kg}}{(\text{height in m})^2}$

The next step is to compare the numerical value of the person's BMI with a table that gives the appropriate classification, such as Table SP8.1. You should note that the BMI formula gives a range of values which are classified as within each category. 'Morbidly obese' indicates that the obesity is classed as an illness. The formula is not suitable for children, pregnant women or for people with certain medical conditions. Additionally, high-performance athletes often have BMI values that lie outside the normal range in either direction, depending on their sport, and there is also a lower threshold for obesity for people from countries such as Japan and Korea, who usually have a smaller frame than Westerners. So BMI values should be used with care in many circumstances and should be treated as no more than a useful guide.

Table SP8.1 Body mass indices and the associated classifications for adults.

Body mass index	Classification
less than 18.5	underweight
18.5–25	desirable or healthy weight
25–30	overweight
30–40	obese
over 40	morbidly or severely obese

Based on estimates of BMI values, about 10% of the world's adult population is obese. In the UK in 1980, 8% of adult women and 6% of adult men were classified as obese but by 2001, this proportion had increased to nearly a quarter of women and 21% of men. Combining the overweight and obese groups, nearly two-thirds of men and over half the women were either overweight or obese. Obesity is also rising in children. In 2001, nearly 9% of 6-year-olds and 15% of 15-year-olds were obese. Projecting the data forwards, by 2020, one-third of adults and possibly half of children in the UK will be obese.

To understand these data fully, you need to be able easily to compare information that is given as fractions, e.g. 'two-thirds of men', with that given as percentages, e.g. '15% of 15-year-olds'. Since the meaning of % is 'in every a hundred', you can read 15% as 15 in every 100, or, written as a fraction $\dfrac{15}{100}$. By dividing the top and bottom numbers by 5, you get $\dfrac{3}{20}$ and if you divide top and bottom by a further 3, you get $\dfrac{1}{\text{almost } 7}$, which you could state as 'about one-seventh'. To convert a fraction to a percentage, multiply the top number by 100 and then divide the bottom number into it. For example, two-thirds becomes

$$\frac{2 \times 100}{3}\% = \frac{200}{3}\% = 67\%$$

If you need more practice in working with fractions and percentages, you should refer to the *Maths Skills Booklet*.

Question SP8.2 Complete Table SP8.2, as far as possible, with the percentage of obesity in the UK population since 1980, based on the figures given in the paragraph above. Use your completed table to answer the following questions:

(a) Do the data support the statement that obesity amongst UK adults has increased by three times (sometimes written as 300%) in the past 20 years?

(b) Similarly, do the data indicate that obesity in children will increase by three times between 2001 and 2020? ◀

Table SP8.2 Obesity in the UK population in 1980 and 2001, with estimates for 2020.

Year	Obesity in various groups in the UK population/%					
	All adults	Men	Women	All children	6-year-olds	15-year-olds
1980						
2001						
2020						

Obesity has been shown in adults to increase with age, and to increase most rapidly when people are in their 20s and early 30s. It is more prevalent in lower socio-economic and lower income groups, particularly amongst women. The rates of obesity in the UK are higher than in many other western European countries, but lower than in the USA.

8.2.2 Health risks of obesity

People in both the overweight and obese categories (based on their BMI) are at an increased risk of developing serious health conditions such as high blood pressure (hypertension), cardiovascular disease, type 2 diabetes and some forms of cancer. These diseases all develop slowly and insidiously. Additionally, there are conditions that are not generally life-threatening, but that do affect well-being, such as arthritis. In fact, both overweight and significantly underweight individuals have an increased risk of premature death, as shown in Figure SP8.1. You will notice that there are no units given on either of the axes; that is because in both cases, they are ratios of one number to another.

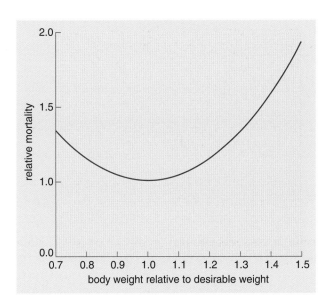

Figure SP8.1 The relationship between actual body weight relative to desirable weight (calculated from BMI), and relative mortality.

● On the horizontal *x*-axis of Figure SP8.1, labelled 'body weight relative to desirable weight', what does a value of 1.4 indicate about the person's weight?

◉ The values given on the *x*-axis are the ratio of the person's weight compared with the ideal weight for that person. So a value of 1.4 would indicate a person who was 1.4 times heavier than their ideal weight. So, if the ideal weight for someone's height and build was 70 kg (about 11 stones), then the actual weight of someone with a body weight to desirable weight ratio of 1.4 would be nearly 100 kg (more than 15 stones).

● What does a value of 1.5 on the 'relative mortality' axis indicate?

◉ A relative mortality value of 1.5 indicates that the person is one and a half times more likely to die at a younger age than would be expected for someone whose weight is close to the ideal value.

The distribution of body fat, as well as the amount, appears to be important in relation to health risk. Fat distribution can be measured either as a ratio of the waist to hip measurements, or simply a waist measurement alone. Men tend to accumulate fat around the abdomen producing an apple-shaped outline (central obesity), whereas women generally accumulate fat around their hips, giving a pear-shaped silhouette (peripheral obesity). After the menopause, women accumulate more fat centrally. This 'central obesity' appears to be linked to higher health risks. Waist to hip ratios of more than 0.95 in men and 0.8 in pre-menopausal women correlate with increased health risks. In many cases, these ratios may be more useful than BMI values for predicting susceptibility to obesity-related disease. If waist measurements alone are used, then less than 94 cm (37 inches) for men or 80 cm (about 31 inches) for women is considered normal. There is an increasing risk for men with a waist measurement of 94–102 cm, and over 102 cm is considered to be high risk. The equivalent measurements for women are 80–88 cm and over 88 cm.

● Would a man with a waist measurement of 118 cm and a hip measurement of 125 cm be considered at risk based on either waist to hip ratio or waist measurement alone?

◐ He would be at high risk with a waist measurement of 118 cm, which is above the 102 cm limit. However, with a waist to hip ratio of $\frac{118\,cm}{125\,cm} = 0.944$, he is below the risk value of 0.95, but only just. Weight reduction is recommended.

8.3   Tackling obesity

The UK House of Commons Health Committee published a report in 2004 in which the increasing problem of obesity was heavily emphasised and subsequent Government initiatives have continued to keep the issue in the public eye. If obesity continues to increase at the current rate, it is expected that it will soon overtake smoking as the biggest lifestyle-related cause of premature loss of life. There is a 9-year reduction in life expectancy for obese individuals. The economic cost of obesity is estimated at around £3.5 billion per year. This cost estimate includes predicted costs to the NHS for treatment of obese patients, as well as time lost to industry due to sickness. So, both for the individual and for society in general, tackling obesity is a major issue. This involves either reducing energy intake ('going on a diet'), increasing energy output (by taking more exercise) or both. These lifestyle changes can be promoted both at the level of the individual and at Government level.

8.3.1   Reducing energy intake

Despite a multitude of different 'diets' being publicised, some more bizarre than others, there is little evidence that any work in any way other than by reducing the energy intake in some way. However, the adult body is so well tuned to keeping weight stable, despite fluctuations in food intake, that losing weight is never easy. Deliberate reduction of food intake leads to sensations of increased hunger, so great willpower is needed to lose weight and it is extremely easy to put the weight back on again. Additionally, when weight is reduced, the body contains relatively less actively metabolising tissue, so the basal metabolic rate is lower and the body needs to take in even less energy to maintain the smaller mass of tissue.

Energy intake can be reduced by changing the composition of food that is eaten, as well as reducing the amount. Current data indicate that high-fat diets are most closely linked to high BMI and that as the proportion of carbohydrate in the diet increases, BMI decreases. However the 'Atkins diet', which gained much publicity in the early 2000s, advocates very low carbohydrate intake and high intakes of fat and protein. It appears to work by altering some metabolic pathways and reducing appetite, so that less energy is taken in overall. However, although effective for weight loss, an extreme diet such as this may have adverse health effects too.

Nevertheless, rises in obesity over the past 50 years do correlate with increasing fat intake and decreasing carbohydrate intake. Fat is low in bulk compared with its energy content, i.e. it has a high energy density, and it is also stored very efficiently in the body. Thus, Government advice on obesity tends to be focused on reducing intake of those foods that have a 'high energy density'. It has been suggested that food could be labelled using a 'traffic light' system, with 'green' for foods of low energy density, 'amber' for medium energy density and 'red' for high energy density. This information might enable the consumer to select more easily the appropriate foods. A reduction in portion sizes for fast-food and other ready-made meals is proposed too. In a particular move to combat childhood obesity, it is proposed that the advertising of 'unhealthy' food on TV when children are likely to be watching, should be banned.

8.3.2 Increasing energy output

Alongside attempting to reduce energy input, obesity can also be tackled by increasing energy output, and increased activity has the greatest potential to achieve this.

- Consider for a moment whether there are any other ways in which energy utilisation can be increased without increasing activity.

- You might have thought of heat production for temperature regulation. If you are very cold, shivering sets in as an automatic response, thus increasing energy expenditure in the form of heat. People who are feeling cold also tend to become more active – stamping their feet, clapping their hands, etc. If you have a major infection, your body temperature rises and again, energy is used to generate heat. The latter, however, is not recommended as a way of combating obesity!

Increased physical activity can take the form of definite amounts of exercise. 30 minutes exercise on 5 days each week is recommended. However, although many people start an exercise programme with great enthusiasm, they are often not able to keep it up on a long-term basis. The exercise needs to be incorporated into the daily routine and Government initiatives plan to encourage such habits in the workplace and in schools. Exercise has the added advantage of raising the BMR for some time, possibly hours, after the exercise has been completed, so using additional energy. In the long-term, exercise increases the ratio of muscle to fat in the body.

- How does an increase in the ratio of muscle tissue to fat affect BMR? You might find it useful to look back at SP7.4.1.

- SP7.4.1 states that 'Adipose tissue (fat) consumes much less energy than a similar mass of muscle and other body tissues. So, the higher the proportion of fat, the lower the metabolic rate of that individual.' So an overweight person whose weight remains constant but who, through exercise, reduces the amount of fat and increases the amount of muscle has a higher BMR and is therefore more likely to lose weight in future.

Of course, although exercise is desirable for overweight and obese individuals, it may be quite difficult. The heavier a person becomes, the more daunting it is to play sport, join a gym, go for a long walk or a swim, or take any other form of exercise. The wrong sort of exercise may cause strain on joints, and pain, which then deters them from exercise in future. Becoming obese can be the start of a downward spiral. Interestingly, low level movement such as fidgeting uses a significant amount of energy and may explain some of the discrepancies in apparent energy output when compared with food intake data in some people.

8.3.3 Other ways of losing weight

An accidental way of losing weight was discovered during World War I. Female munitions workers, packing an explosive called 2,4-dinitrophenol (2,4-DNP) into shells, suffered from significant, sometimes fatal, weight loss. It was discovered that this chemical affected the ability of the cells in their body to link the breakdown of glucose to the production of a vital molecule which the body uses as a very short-term energy store, called ATP (adenosine triphosphate) (you will learn more about ATP in SP16.5). Once the two processes were uncoupled, glucose was broken down in the normal way, but only heat was produced without any biologically useful energy. So the body used fat stores to attempt to generate more ATP, with the effect that the body gradually 'wasted away'. Further investigations have been undertaken to develop a similar 'uncoupling' agent with less drastic effects for use as a 'diet pill', but with no success so far.

Other studies have identified a medium-sized protein called leptin which is produced by adipose tissue (fat) in the body. Levels of leptin in the blood vary on a 24-hour cycle and high levels tend to be present after eating, with low levels during fasting. Low levels appear to trigger a feeling of hunger by increasing the sensitivity of the response to the gut hormone CCK (see SP2.3). However, it has not proved possible to use leptin as a drug to suppress appetite, although work continues on the molecule itself and how it functions in the body. Only in a very few individuals has it been possible to link faults in leptin production or activity to their predisposition to obesity.

Two classes of drugs, both unrelated to those mentioned in the previous paragraphs, have recently been made available to obese patients in the UK to assist in losing weight. The following question looks at information on one of these.

Question SP8.3 In 2001, a drug called sibutramine (with the trademark Meridia), which works by suppressing appetite, was licensed by NICE (the National Institute for Health and Clinical Excellence) in the UK. Here is part of the guidance to the medical profession for its use:

1.1   Sibutramine should be prescribed only as part of an overall treatment plan for management of nutritional obesity in people aged 18–65 years who meet one of the following criteria:

1.1.1   A body mass index (BMI) of $27.0 \ kg/m^2$ or more in the presence of significant co-morbidities

1.1.2   A BMI of $30.0 \ kg/m^2$ or more without associated co-morbidities

1.2   Sibutramine should be prescribed, in accordance with the Summary of Product Characteristics, only for people who have previously made serious attempts to lose weight by diet, exercise and/or other behavioural modifications.

1.3   When treatment with sibutramine is offered, arrangements should be made for appropriate health professionals to offer specific concomitant advice, support and counselling on diet, physical activity and behavioural strategies. Sibutramine should not be prescribed unless adequate arrangements for monitoring both weight loss and adverse effects can be made available.

Note that 'co-morbidity' means the presence of another condition or disease alongside the first one, in this case alongside obesity.

(a) What do you notice about the way that the values for BMI have been expressed?

(b) Using the information on BMI values in Table SP8.1, how would the people mentioned in paragraphs 1.1.1 and 1.1.2 be classified?

(c) Which groups of people are excluded from receiving sibutramine?

(d) Do doctors expect sibutramine to be free of side-effects? ◄

A second type of drug is Orlistat (also known as Xenical), which works by inhibiting the enzyme pancreatic lipase.

●   Where is pancreatic lipase produced in the body and what is its action? (Use the *Glossary* or look back at SP5.5).

◐   Pancreatic lipase is an enzyme produced by the pancreas and released into the small intestine. It breaks up triacylglycerols into two fatty acids and one monoacylglycerol. These smaller molecules can then be absorbed into the cells lining the intestine where they are reconverted into triacylglycerols which pass to the bloodstream for use, or storage, in the body.

●   If Orlistat inhibits this enzyme, how does its use help with weight loss? What side effects might the drug have?

◐   Since Orlistat prevents the digestion of fat, and therefore its absorption into the cells and then the blood, fat in the diet remains in the gut contents and is lost from the body in the faeces. The reduced amount of fat taken up by the body should help with weight loss. The presence of more fat than normal in the faeces can cause them to be loose and oily, resulting in hurried visits to the toilet.

Like sibutramine, Orlistat is prescribed only to those who have already made serious attempts to lose weight by other means. It has proved effective in some patients, though when treatment with the drug ends, these individuals often regain the lost weight. In other patients, it has had little effect, possibly because they allow themselves to eat more because they know they are unlikely to put on more weight. Its unfortunate side-effect may be the most effective action of the drug. Those people who eat a high-fat diet find the need for urgent visits to the toilet when they are taking Orlistat, a great encouragement to reduce the amount of fat in their diet!

Surgery can be used as a drastic way to curtail food intake and so lose weight, but again, it needs to be used alongside other methods of weight reduction. Surgery in an obese patient has considerable risks due to the strain it puts on the heart and so it is not commonly undertaken in the UK. The jaws can be wired together to restrict eating; the effective stomach size can be reduced by stapling or inserting a balloon, so that only small meals can be eaten before the patient feels full; or parts of the digestive system can be temporarily bypassed to prevent absorption of food into the body.

Fat can also be surgically removed from the abdomen. Cosmetic surgery such as liposuction to remove fat from the thighs or buttocks removes only relatively small amounts of fat and makes little difference to overall weight (though it can improve appearance).

8.4 Inadequate weight

Although in the UK obesity is the main problem, elsewhere in the world millions of people face starvation and well over 5 million, mostly children, die each year from inadequate nutrient intake. People who are starving, or even those who are apparently eating sufficient quantities of food but do not have a balanced diet, are susceptible to a variety of other illnesses due to their impaired immune system. You may recall from SP5.6 that fat has important roles in maintaining the immune system.

Illness itself can be a cause of inadequate food intake. Various illnesses, both physical and psychological, and some medical treatments, are accompanied by a loss of appetite, and if low food intake persists, malnutrition (defined as an inadequate intake of essential nutrients) can ensue. In some types of cancer, chemicals produced by the tumour cells can cause changes to the body's metabolism with the result that, even with an adequate diet, severe weight loss occurs (cancer cachexia).

The condition in which a person demonstrates an extreme aversion to food is called anorexia nervosa. In the UK, it usually affects females from their teenage years until their 30s (only 5% of people with anorexia nervosa are male) and may be accompanied by bulimia nervosa where the person eats huge quantities of food and then gets rid of it before it is absorbed properly, by vomiting or the use of laxatives. Despite considerable research, no effective way of preventing these disorders has been found and treatment by both clinical and psychological strategies is lengthy and not always successful.

Summary of SP8

1 Obesity, measured as a body mass index (BMI) of over 30, is increasing rapidly in the UK.

2 Obesity increases the risk of developing many serious health problems, such as hypertension, cardiovascular disease and diabetes.

3 Weight can be reduced by reducing energy intake, by changing the composition of food in the diet, eating less and increasing energy output by taking more exercise.

4 Some drugs are also available that may assist in weight loss.

Vitamins

STUDY PERIOD 9

9.1 Introduction

Before the 19th century, one of the hazards of long sea voyages was a condition called scurvy, whose symptoms were loss of hair and teeth, bleeding gums, very slow healing of wounds and eventually death. Hundreds of sailors and explorers died from scurvy until a Scottish physician, James Lind, in the 1750s discovered that adding a daily portion of citrus fruit to the rations of those at sea could prevent the condition, whereas adding cider, vinegar or various other substances that he tested, could not. In those days, it was considered that a disease was caused by something bad in the diet, or in the air, but not by the absence of something good, so despite Lind's evidence, his ideas were not accepted by his fellow physicians. Additionally, he was unable to confirm his work by experiments on land since, although he tried to restrict the types of food eaten by a group of volunteers to attempt to produce scurvy in them, he was unable to do so, probably because it can take several months for the condition to develop and in that time, his volunteers occasionally cheated on their diet. However, though he died disillusioned, Lind had actually discovered the importance and source of vitamin C.

The term 'vitamin' was not coined until early in the 20th century, to describe those chemicals in food without which a pattern of deficiency symptoms (often called a deficiency syndrome) occurs. Vitamins were named by being given a letter, before their detailed chemical structures were known and so they are still referred to by that letter, as well as by their chemical name; for example, vitamin C or ascorbic acid.

Vitamins are divided into two main groups: the fat-soluble vitamins A, D, E and K, and the water-soluble vitamins, those of the B group (numbered B_1, B_2, etc.) and vitamin C. The body can store fat-soluble vitamins, but any excess water-soluble vitamins are easily removed from the body in the urine, so regular intake is necessary. Vitamins are, however, needed in only very small quantities.

● How many milligrams are there in one gram? Check in the *Maths Skills Booklet* or look back to SP6.2.1.

● There are 1000 mg in one gram. 1 mg is one-thousandth of a gram.

The daily requirement of certain vitamins is much less than 1 mg and so is measured in micrograms per day, written as µg per day, where 1 µg is one-thousandth of a milligram. The values for the daily requirements of vitamins are regularly updated as more information becomes available. The values given in Table SP9.1 are those recommended by the UK Government's Food Standards Agency early in 2005.

Table SP9.1 Vitamins essential for human health, reference nutrient intake (RNI) values taken from the UK Food Standards Agency website, and the main dietary sources of these vitamins.

Name	RNI values for adults per day	Main dietary sources
Fat-soluble vitamins		
vitamin A	0.6 mg for women 0.7 mg for men	liver, cheese, eggs, butter, oily fish (such as mackerel), milk, fortified* margarine, yoghurt
vitamin D	0.01 mg (10 µg) for certain groups, e.g. pregnant women, those who rarely go outside, etc.	oily fish, liver, eggs, margarine, some breakfast cereals, bread, powdered milk
vitamin E	3 mg for women 4 mg for men	plant oils (such as soya, corn and olive oil), nuts, seeds, wheatgerm, some green leafy vegetables
vitamin K	0.07 mg (70 µg), or 1 µg per kg of body weight	green leafy vegetables (such as broccoli and spinach), vegetable oils, cereals; small amounts can also be found in meat (such as pork), and dairy foods (such as cheese)
Water-soluble vitamins		
thiamin (vitamin B_1)	0.8 mg for women 1 mg for men	pork, vegetables, milk, cheese, peas, fresh and dried fruit, eggs, wholegrain breads, some fortified* breakfast cereals
riboflavin (vitamin B_2)	1.1 mg for women 1.3 mg for men	milk, eggs, fortified* breakfast cereals, rice, mushrooms.
niacin (vitamin B_3)	13 mg for women 17 mg for men	beef, pork, chicken, wheat flour, maize flour, eggs, milk
vitamin B_6 (pyridoxine)	1.2 mg for women 1.4 mg for men	liver, pork, chicken, turkey, cod, bread, whole cereals (such as oatmeal, wheatgerm and rice), eggs, vegetables, soya beans, peanuts, milk, potatoes, breakfast cereals
folate (folic acid, vitamin B_9)	0.2 mg, but 0.4 mg extra for women who are, or plan to be, pregnant	broccoli, sprouts, spinach, peas, chick peas, potatoes, yeast extract, brown rice, some fruit (such as oranges and bananas), breakfast cereals, some bread
vitamin B_{12} (cobalamin)	0.0015 mg (1.5 µg)	meat (particularly liver), salmon, cod, milk, cheese, eggs, yeast extract, some breakfast cereals
pantothenic acid (vitamin B_5)	none given – should be sufficient in normal diet	chicken, beef, potatoes, porridge, tomatoes, liver, kidneys, eggs, broccoli, whole grains (such as brown rice and wholemeal bread), some breakfast cereals
biotin (vitamin H)	0.01–0.2 mg	meat (such as kidney and liver), eggs and some fruit and vegetables, especially dried mixed fruit
vitamin C (ascorbic acid)	40 mg	wide variety of fruit and vegetables, especially peppers, broccoli, sprouts, sweet potatoes, cranberries, citrus fruits, kiwi fruit

* 'Fortified' indicates that the vitamin has been added during manufacture of the food product.

Question SP9.1 Use Table SP9.1 to answer the following questions.

(a) Which vitamin is needed in the greatest daily amount and how much of that vitamin is needed?

(b) Which other vitamins are needed by men in amounts of more than 1 mg per day?

(c) Which vitamins are needed in amounts of 100 μg or less per day? ◀

Question SP9.2 On a breakfast cereal packet, the nutrition information states that a 40 g serving of the cereal, with 125 g semi-skimmed milk, provides the following vitamins:

Vitamins	Amount per serving	% RDA
thiamin (B_1)	0.4 mg	30
riboflavin (B_2)	0.6 mg	40
niacin	4.6 mg	25
vitamin B_6	0.6 mg	30
folic acid	110 μg	55
vitamin B_{12}	0.75 μg	75

(a) What is meant by % RDA in the heading of the third column here?

(b) What is the RDA of thiamin in mg? How does this value compare with the information in Table SP9.1? Suggest possible reasons for any difference.

(c) Based on the information in Table SP9.1, which of these vitamins are likely to be present only in the cereal, which only in the milk and which could be present in both? ◀

Question SP9.3 Looking down the main dietary sources of the vitamins in Table SP9.1, which one food contains the most vitamins? Which vitamins does this food *not* contain? Suggest an explanation for why this food is so rich in vitamins. ◀

The following sections consider the fat-soluble vitamins and then the water-soluble ones in turn. Vitamins have complex chemical structures, and so, apart from a brief look at vitamin A, we will not be dealing with their chemistry here.

9.2 Vitamin A

● Look back at Table SP9.1 and identify the foods that contain vitamin A. On the basis of this information, try to predict where vitamin A is stored in the human body.

◔ Vitamin A is found in liver. If it is stored in the liver of other animals that we eat, then it would be reasonable to suggest that it might be stored in human liver, which indeed it is. Since vitamin A is a fat-soluble vitamin, you might also predict that it would be stored in adipose tissue, which, to a lesser extent, it is too.

Vitamin A is toxic if taken in very large quantities and poisoning has occurred in Arctic explorers who have eaten polar bear liver, which is particularly rich in vitamin A. The concentration of vitamin A in lamb and calf liver has increased substantially in the last 20 years due to supplements to their feed. Pregnant women are advised to restrict their intake of liver and pâté made from liver, since there is some evidence that high doses of vitamin A can cause birth defects. However, vitamin A is an essential part of the human diet and severe health problems occur if there is a deficiency. Since dairy products, such as butter, are a good source of vitamin A, all types of margarine and similar spreads are now required by law to have vitamin A added to them, as you will see on their labels. Vitamin A, which is actually a group of interrelated substances (retinol, retinal and retinoic acid), can be synthesised in the body from β-carotene, found in dark-green leafy vegetables such as cabbage, sprouts, broccoli and spinach, and in carrots. Cooking the vegetables does not damage the β-carotene molecules and in fact β-carotene is more easily absorbed into the body from cooked carrots. The structure of β-carotene, retinol and retinal are shown in Figure SP9.1.

Figure SP9.1 Chemical structure of (a) β-carotene, (b) retinol and (c) retinal. Note that for ease of comparison, the carbon atoms, with their associated hydrogen atoms, have been omitted from the chains and the rings.

● Look carefully at the three molecules and identify the relationship between retinol and β-carotene and the difference between retinal and retinol.

● If a β-carotene molecule (a) is split in the middle and a molecule of water (H_2O) added to each cut end, then two molecules of retinol (b) are produced. Retinol is the same as retinal (c) except that two hydrogen atoms have been removed from the end of the molecule to give a –CHO group, rather than a –CH$_2$OH group.

Retinal is found in the cells of the eye where it plays a vital part in the perception of light and this is the reason why the 'old wives' tale' that carrots help you to see in the dark is, in fact, true. The speed at which the human eye adapts to seeing in the dark depends on the amount of vitamin A available in the body, known as the vitamin A status. A 'dark adaptation test' can be used as a measure of vitamin A status. Vitamin A deficiency is a major public health problem in the developing world, causing blindness in a quarter of a million people each year. Vitamin A supplements are successful in preventing blindness from this cause.

Vitamin A also assists in keeping the epithelial cells of the body moist and healthy.

● Where have you already met cells described as 'epithelium'?

● In SP5.5, the lining of the small intestine was described as an epithelium, made up of epithelial cells (as drawn in Figure SP1.1b).

As well as lining the whole of the digestive tract, epithelial cells also cover the surfaces of the glands around the eyes and line the lungs (and are found elsewhere too). Xerophthalmia or dry-eye is a classic sign of vitamin A deficiency. Tear production is reduced and the eyes become susceptible to infections such as conjunctivitis. Children who are vitamin A-deficient are more susceptible to respiratory infections and measles. Vitamin A is involved in normal growth and bone formation and it plays a part in the production of red blood cells and therefore the prevention of anaemia.

In order to understand another important role of vitamin A, and other vitamins, as antioxidants, you need to know a little more about the internal structure of atoms. You will recall that atoms sometimes carry a positive or a negative (+ or −) charge (SP4.6.1 discussed the charges on R groups of certain amino acids). These charges arise because atoms are made up of positively charged particles called protons and negatively charged particles called electrons. The protons, along with uncharged particles called neutrons, reside in the core of the atom as part of the atomic nucleus. For the purpose of this simple description, you can think of the electrons as tiny spheres that are in orbit around the nucleus. Normally, the numbers of protons and electrons in any particular atom are the same, so the positive and negative charges are balanced, and overall the atom has no charge. However, if an atom gains an electron, it has one extra negative charge (since it now has one more electron than it has protons), and so we would write a − sign beside it, and if it loses an electron, it has a positive charge (since it now has one more proton than it has electrons), and we would write + beside it. When atoms bond together, they can share pairs of electrons, one from each atom, so when we have been talking about a bond between two atoms (the atoms 'holding hands'), we have actually been referring to these electron pairs.

However, sometimes a molecule can be formed in which there is an atom with a single free electron, and this type of molecule is called a free radical. Free radicals are extremely reactive and the problem is that as they react, they create more and more free radicals in a runaway chain reaction. This process happening within cells involves atoms in molecules such as DNA that are vital to the cell's functioning, and it can have serious health consequences. The precise way in which free radicals cause the damage attributed to them is not fully understood, but they are implicated in many human diseases and disorders. Many pollutants generate free radicals, as does smoking, and free radicals are probably the link between exposure to toxins and the development of cancer.

Certain molecules have the ability to donate electrons to free radicals, while not themselves being destroyed or becoming free radicals. Thus they can safely interact with free radicals and terminate the chain reactions before vital cell components are damaged or destroyed. Such molecules are known as antioxidants, and vitamin A is one of the important antioxidants in the body.

9.3   Vitamin D

The main role of vitamin D is to facilitate the uptake of calcium from food, through the lining of the small intestine into the blood. It also controls the deposition of calcium in the bones during growth and maintains adult bone structure. If vitamin D is deficient, with less calcium available, the skeleton fails to develop normally. The most obvious symptom is the bowing of the leg bones in children, producing the condition called rickets (Figure SP9.2). Children with vitamin D deficiency grow more slowly and may become smaller adults which, in women, has serious consequences because the pelvis may end up so small that giving birth normally is impossible. Vitamin D deficiency in adults is called osteomalacia. Rickets and osteomalacia were relatively common in Europe during the 19th century, especially in urban slums.

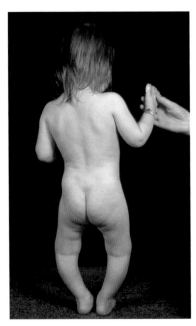

Figure SP9.2 A young child with rickets photographed in the late 1980s; without sufficient vitamin D, calcium is not properly absorbed in the gut so the growing bones cannot harden normally. The abnormally flexible bones bend under the child's weight, producing the characteristic bowed legs.

● Given that vitamin D is a fat-soluble vitamin, predict which foods are likely to contain it.

◐ You would expect to find vitamin D in those foods that contain significant amounts of fat, such as dairy products and, by analogy with vitamin A, probably liver too.

If you check back to Table SP9.1, you will find oily fish on the list and you may know that a generation or two ago, a regular dose of cod liver oil was given to children to prevent rickets. Levels of vitamin D in dairy products vary throughout the year but it is now added to margarine and many low-fat spreads, providing an all-year-round supply. Breakfast cereals, yoghurts and food for babies and infants are often also 'fortified' with vitamin D.

However, there is some debate as to whether vitamin D should actually be classified as a vitamin, since it does not fit completely with the usual definition, which is that vitamins are obtained from the diet. It is not essential to obtain vitamin D in the diet. It can be synthesised below the surface of the skin in the presence of ultraviolet (UV-B) light. However, in the UK, there is insufficient UV-B in sunlight between October and March for synthesis to occur, although most people probably make and store enough in the body during the summer months to last through the winter.

● Which groups of people would be most at risk if their diet contained insufficient vitamin D?

◐ You might have thought of: people who are housebound during the summer; people who live in areas of high air pollution; those who never expose their skin to sunlight or only do so when wearing high factor (UV-B blocking) sunscreens; and people with dark skin which prevents the UV light from penetrating far enough into the skin for vitamin D synthesis.

In fact, the beneficial effect of sunlight, in playing a part in vitamin D synthesis, has to be balanced with the detrimental effect, its role in causing skin cancers. It appears that an exposure to sunlight of about 30 minutes per day (avoiding the part of the day when sunlight is strongest) is an appropriate balance between the harmful and beneficial effects. Although rickets has largely been eliminated in the UK, due to the addition of vitamin D to food especially for infants and children, the condition has reappeared in Asian communities in the UK, especially in the more northern parts of the country.

● List the factors, relating to both dietary intake and production of vitamin D, that may be the cause of vitamin D deficiency in Asian communities.

● Some of the factors are:
  - darker skin colour, so that more exposure to sunlight is required to stimulate vitamin D production
  - less sunlight in northern parts of the UK than in the south, or than would be found in the Asian countries from where this population group originated
  - for cultural reasons, spending less time out of doors than white UK residents, (such habits are especially common among Asian women)
  - the wearing of clothes that cover more of the body surface than those of white UK residents, so exposing less skin to sunlight
  - a diet containing less dairy products than a typical UK diet; a strict vegetarian diet is particularly low in vitamin D.

9.4 Vitamin E

Vitamin E is not a single compound, but consists of a group of eight closely related chemicals, of which the most important, responsible for about 90% of its activity in the body is alpha-tocopherol. Since, like vitamins A and D, vitamin E is fat-soluble, it occurs in fat-rich foods. The main sources in the UK diet are from plant oils such as soya, corn and olive oil. Other good sources include nuts and seeds, and wheatgerm (the part of the wheat grain that will develop into the new plant) and some green leafy vegetables. It is added to some margarines and spreads.

The main role of vitamin E in the body is as an antioxidant.

Question SP9.4 Fill in the blanks in the following short paragraph. You may need to look back to the end of SP9.2.

Some chemical reactions in the body produce harmful substances called _____

_____ that contain single _____ and become involved in chain reactions

in the cells, which can be damaging to the body. _____ like

vitamins _____ and_____ neutralise the harmful substances and prevent

further damage. ◀

Vitamin E is particularly important in maintaining cell membranes in a healthy state. Its presence appears to be particularly significant in the lungs, red blood cells, heart and brain, though deficiencies are rare and few human conditions can be specifically related to its absence. However, fewer cases of heart disease and cancer occur in people whose vitamin E intake is adequate. There is, as yet, no clear evidence that taking in additional vitamin E gives additional protection against these conditions and supplements are not advised.

9.5　Vitamin K

Like vitamin E, vitamin K is fat-soluble and composed of a series of related compounds. Vitamin K is widely distributed in the diet (see Table SP9.1) and it is absorbed from the small intestine with the assistance of bile acids. Vitamin K is also manufactured by the bacteria that inhabit the human large intestine and appears to be absorbed there too. The main role of vitamin K is in blood clotting. This process requires the presence of a number of different chemicals, called clotting factors, in the blood. A number of these (including prothrombin and Factors VII, IX and X) require vitamin K in their synthesis. Deficiency could therefore result in an increasing tendency to bleed. Vitamin K also plays a role in the formation of bone and supplements can be effective in increasing bone density in osteoporosis.

● How might a course of antibiotics affect the levels of vitamin K in the blood?

◐ Antibiotics kill bacteria, so, as well as destroying those that are causing the infection for which the antibiotics have been prescribed, they also kill many of the useful bacteria in the gut. Since these bacteria synthesise vitamin K, their absence could lead to reduced vitamin K uptake from the gut into the blood for a few days until the normal population of bacteria in the gut is re-established.

There is a rare condition called vitamin K deficiency bleeding which occurs in about 1 in 10 000 babies in the first few weeks of life. Many babies who have this condition die or sustain significant brain damage due to bleeding into the brain. The condition occurs almost exclusively in breastfed babies, since human milk contains very little vitamin K, whereas it is added to formula milk. It is almost completely preventable by giving a single injection of vitamin K soon after birth, and such an injection has been given routinely to UK babies since the 1960s. However, two papers in the early 1990s suggested an association between the vitamin K injection and a very slight increase in the incidence of childhood leukaemia. This discovery led, in some countries, to vitamin K being offered as an oral dose instead. However, vitamin K by mouth was less effective than the injection at preventing vitamin K deficiency bleeding, which still occurred in 1 in 100 000 babies. Other research has not supported the link between vitamin K and leukaemia and a study published in 2004, which looked at 4000 cases of child-hood cancers, found no association with the injections of vitamin K. In the UK now, new mothers may be given the choice of a vitamin K injection or a course of oral doses for their newborn baby.

● Check back to the start of SP9.2 and list the vitamins that have been covered so far. Which group remain?

◓ So far we have covered vitamins A, D, E and K – the fat-soluble vitamins. The group that remains is the water-soluble group of vitamins, vitamins B and C.

9.6 Vitamin B

Vitamin B, often called the vitamin B complex, consists of a whole range of different compounds, some of which have similar functions and work together. However, unlike the families of compounds forming vitamins E and K, the B vitamins are sufficiently different from one another to be given individual names or numbers, and to be listed separately on many food labels. Except for vitamin B_{12}, the body can only store limited amounts of B vitamins and because they are all water-soluble, any excess is excreted in the urine. Their water-solubility also means that B vitamins are easily lost in cooking, and they can also be destroyed by light and exposure to air.

9.6.1 Thiamin (or thiamine, also known as vitamin B_1)

The deficiency disease beriberi has been known for thousands of years. The name literally means 'I can't, I can't' in Sinhalese (a major language in Sri Lanka), and reflects the crippling effect on its victims, who suffer from neurological symptoms, including pain, fatigue and paralysis, and cardiovascular disease. The disease was most common in southeast Asia, where white or 'polished' rice was a major part of the diet. The main source of thiamin is in the outer layers of the grain, the bran, which is removed during milling to produce white rice grain and white rice flour. Thiamin is added to white flour in the UK and many breakfast cereals are also enriched in thiamin. It is present in seeds, nuts and in beans and in smaller quantities in other foods such as meat, milk and potatoes. Since potatoes are eaten frequently in the UK diet, they can form a useful source, though thiamin is gradually destroyed by boiling water and it is estimated that 20% of the possible dietary intake is lost in cooking.

Thiamin is essential in many of the metabolic pathways in the body, especially in the processing of carbohydrate to provide energy. Since the nervous system relies almost exclusively on carbohydrate (glucose) for its energy, it is not surprising that the symptoms of deficiency are seen there. Because, as a water-soluble vitamin, little thiamin can be stored in the body, symptoms appear in less than a month on a diet in which it is completely absent. The early symptoms can, however, be rapidly corrected by regular intake of thiamin.

There are two forms of beriberi, known as the 'wet' and 'dry' forms. In 'wet' beriberi, there is swelling of the limbs, increased heart rate, lung congestion and an enlarged heart, all symptoms of heart failure, which can ultimately be fatal. The symptoms of 'dry' beriberi include pain, tingling and loss of sensation in the hands and feet, muscle wasting and gradual loss of function and paralysis of the legs, brain damage and eventually death. Nowadays, with better nutritional information and the addition of thiamin to many foods, beriberi is rarely seen, except in people with alcoholism, who mainly have the 'dry' form, in a condition called Wernicke–Korsakoff syndrome. Chronic alcoholism is often associated with poor nutrition and therefore a low intake of thiamin. Additionally, alcohol appears to interfere with thiamin absorption from the gut. The symptoms of Wernicke–Korsakoff syndrome begin with peripheral nerve damage (loss of feeling in hands and feet), then damage to the central nervous system and finally a confused mental state, or psychosis, which affects mood, language and thinking.

Because of its involvement in carbohydrate metabolism, additional thiamin may be needed during pregnancy, lactation and also in cancer patients and in people on kidney dialysis. It has been suggested that additional thiamin could be beneficial to performance in certain sports, but experiments so far have produced no evidence to support this idea.

9.6.2 Riboflavin (vitamin B₂)

Riboflavin or vitamin B_2, which was originally known as vitamin G, is found in a wide variety of foods, including milk and dairy products. It is more stable to heat than some of the other B vitamins, but is destroyed by exposure to sunlight. Milk in a glass bottle exposed to sun, loses 10% of its riboflavin per hour. Riboflavin plays a crucial role in the metabolism of carbohydrates and proteins and is involved in many other metabolic reactions in the body.

Although riboflavin deficiency does occur in some parts of the world, it is usually associated with deficiencies in other B vitamins and a specific deficiency syndrome is hard to identify. The clearest signs of deficiency are in the mouth, with cracks and inflammation at the corners, sore and ulcerated lips and a painful tongue. Others signs are detected in the eyes, with increased sensitivity to light and burning and itching sensations.

9.6.3 Niacin (vitamin B₃)

Niacin, which comprises two compounds, nicotinic acid and nicotinamide, also occurs widely in food and is added to many breakfast cereals. It is easily absorbed into the blood from the digestive system and plays a vital role in energy production in cells. It appears to reduce the levels of LDLs in the blood and increase HDLs, perhaps by affecting the proteins that carry the fats.

● Look back to SP5.4.3 to identify the significance of this effect on blood lipoproteins.

● LDLs or low density lipoproteins are a way of transporting cholesterol around in the blood. Cells that need cholesterol take it up from LDLs. If cells contain excess cholesterol, it is returned to the blood packaged into HDLs or high density lipoproteins. The higher the ratio of HDL to LDL in the blood, the lower the risk of developing heart disease. Thus if niacin increases HDLs and reduces LDLs, this should give some protection against heart disease.

The deficiency disease associated with lack of niacin is pellagra. Its symptoms are the four Ds – diarrhoea, dermatitis, dementia and death, normally experienced in that order! The term 'pellagra' was first used in 1771 to describe the disease that was endemic at that time in poor populations in southern Europe. 'Pellagra' is from the Italian words *pelle* meaning 'skin' and *agro* meaning 'sour' and refers to the thickened, roughened skin, or dermatitis which is characteristic of the disease.

It was noticed that people with pellagra subsisted on a diet that was based on maize and contained very little meat. By 1900, the disease had spread to France, Egypt and England and in 1902, it was first reported in America. For the next 20 years, it reached epidemic proportions in the southern USA. Again, poverty and the consumption of large quantities of maize (corn) appeared to be the risk factors. Although it was soon realised that the deficiency disease could be prevented by the inclusion of meat in the diet, it was not until the late 1930s that the explanation of the link with eating a lot of maize was understood.

● This link involves a molecule called tryptophan, which has been mentioned before. Look back at Table SP4.3 and identify what type of molecule tryptophan is.

● Tryptophan is an amino acid, one of the molecules that make up proteins.

Niacin can be synthesised in the body from tryptophan, which is commonly found in animal proteins. In fact, in the average UK diet, there is probably sufficient protein to satisfy all the niacin requirement of the body, and dietary niacin is therefore not essential. However, maize contains so little tryptophan that there is insufficient for the body to convert to niacin. Additionally, any niacin present in the maize itself is so tightly bound to molecules in the maize which are not digested, that it cannot be absorbed by the body. In the indigenous populations of Mexico and Central America, who also subsist on a diet of maize, there have been almost no occurrences of pellagra. It seems that their tradition of soaking the maize in an alkaline solution of lime before cooking it, releases the bound niacin, freeing it for absorption by the body. Poor peasants of the Deccan Plateau of India, however, do suffer from pellagra, although their staple carbohydrate is millet (sorghum) rather than maize. This grain contains sufficient tryptophan but it also contains very high levels of leucine, another amino acid that has been found to prevent niacin synthesis in the body, so symptoms of its deficiency occur. People with HIV infection can also suffer from a pellagra-like condition, since the infection causes the tryptophan levels in their blood to be very low. High doses of niacin can reverse the pellagra condition.

9.6.4 Vitamin B$_6$ (pyridoxine)

Vitamin B$_6$ is composed of pyridoxine and two closely related compounds. It is found in small quantities in many foods, though it can be destroyed in the cooking process. No clear deficiency disease has been recognised in humans as being directly caused by lack of this vitamin, since it is often found in conjunction with other B vitamins and their absence has greater effects. Its main role is in the conversion of some amino acids into other ones, depending on the requirements of the body. It also plays a role in fat metabolism (in the conversion of linoleic acid to arachidonic acid) and in carbohydrate metabolism. Thus deficiency causes generalised problems such as anaemia, dermatitis and neuromuscular problems such as headaches, aching muscles and difficulty in walking. There is some evidence that low doses of vitamin B$_6$ can be helpful in improving the symptoms of premenstrual syndrome (PMS), even when there is no evidence of deficiency in the diet.

9.6.5 Folate (folic acid, vitamin B$_9$)

Folate is a generic name for a group of related compounds. The name 'folate' was based on the word 'foliage', after it was identified in a crude extract from spinach, though it is also found in liver, other green vegetables, oranges and potatoes and it is often added to breakfast cereals (usually listed as folic acid). Folate is less sensitive to heat than many of the B vitamins, though it is destroyed if food is reheated or kept hot for long periods. Folate is involved in amino acid metabolism, but its crucial role is in cell division, since it is used in DNA synthesis. So deficiency of folate has its major effect on dividing cells, especially those in the bone marrow (which produces red blood cells) and those lining the digestive system. Failure of normal cell division in the cells lining the digestive system can lead to loss of appetite, nausea and diarrhoea, and soreness in the mouth. Failure of normal cell division in the bone marrow leads to a type of anaemia called megaloblastic anaemia, where large, immature blood cells which do not have the normal oxygen-carrying capacity, are released into the circulation. After iron deficiency, folate deficiency is the next most common cause of anaemia.

Due to the huge amount of cell division that goes on in the first few months of pregnancy, pregnant women need as much as five times more folate than the normal daily requirement. Up to 25% of women would show changes in their bone marrow that are characteristic of folate deficiency if they did not increase their intake. Folate also appears to be important around the time of conception. For this reason, women planning to become pregnant are now encouraged to take folate supplements for about three months before conception and for the first three months of pregnancy. There appears to be a link between lack of folate and neural tube defects such as spina bifida, where the spinal cord does not develop correctly in the early fetus. Several studies have shown that giving folate supplements to women who have previously given birth to a child with a neural tube defect can reduce the risk of the same problem arising in a subsequent pregnancy by almost 75%.

There is some evidence that folate deficiency is also linked with increased risk of cardiovascular disease and with cancer, but more work is needed in both these areas. Alcohol affects the uptake of folate from the digestive system into the blood; so alcoholics are at risk of folate deficiency for this reason as well as because their diet may be lacking in folate. Other population groups who do not have a balanced diet, due to poverty, poor food choices, or illness, may also be at risk. Some commonly used drugs, including aspirin, indigestion remedies and the contraceptive pill, together with some antibiotics and anti-epilepsy drugs, may affect folate uptake too, and smokers may need additional folate. Chemotherapy drugs used in cancer treatment can also cause folate deficiency. In fact, folate deficiency is probably the most common vitamin deficiency seen in the developed world.

9.6.6 Vitamin B$_{12}$ (cobalamin)

Vitamin B$_{12}$ is yet another group of compounds, this time with an atom of the metal called cobalt (present in only trace quantities in the body) in their structure, hence the alternative name 'cobalamin'. Vitamin B$_{12}$ works alongside folate and if levels of it are low, folate deficiency symptoms occur too. It is stored in the liver and in general the body does not appear to need a regular intake. Many people have enough B_{12} stored in their liver to last for up to 30 years. Unlike most vitamins, vitamin B_{12} is found only in foods obtained from animals. In ruminant animals such as cattle and sheep, the bacteria in their stomachs synthesise vitamin B_{12}, hence its presence in their meat, milk and dairy products. They too store it in their liver and hence eating liver is a rich source of the vitamin. Vegetarians are likely to take in sufficient vitamin B_{12} due to contamination of their food by yeasts and bacteria but strict vegans may need to supplement their diet to ensure sufficient intake. If the diet contains excess amounts of vitamin C, this can bind to vitamin B_{12} and limit its availability. Vitamin B_{12} is essential for the formation of the protective coating of myelin, which is found around some nerve fibres (neurons) and so its deficiency can lead to malfunction of the nerves and eventual paralysis and dementia. Like folate, vitamin B_{12} is also vital for cell division, especially in the bone marrow, since it also plays a role in DNA synthesis.

● What condition might you expect to see in a person with vitamin B_{12} deficiency?

◑ Since red blood cells are produced in the bone marrow (SP1.7), you would expect some type of anaemia to develop.

Deficiency of vitamin B_{12} due to dietary insufficiency is uncommon, but this vitamin can be deficient due to a condition that prevents its normal absorption. Because the B_{12} molecule is particularly large, in order to be absorbed by the body it has to be linked to a protein known as 'intrinsic factor', which is produced by the lining of the stomach. The combined 'complex' is then absorbed into the blood when the food reaches the small intestine. If the cells that produce intrinsic factor are destroyed, or the intrinsic factor is inactivated, vitamin B_{12} cannot be absorbed. This situation may occur due to an autoimmune disease in which the body produces antibodies against the cells that produce the intrinsic factor or against the intrinsic factor itself. Women are more commonly affected than men and this type of autoimmunity tends to run in families. The intrinsic factor-producing cells can also fail to function efficiently in a patient with ulcers, stomach cancer or other conditions such as Crohn's disease that affect the digestive system. The condition that results in all these cases is called pernicious anaemia, for which the treatment is regular injections of vitamin B_{12}.

● Before the availability of injectable vitamin B_{12}, the treatment for pernicious anaemia was to feed the patient large quantities of raw liver every day. Why would this treatment be only partly effective?

◑ The cause of pernicious anaemia is a failure in the absorption of vitamin B_{12} from the food, due to the lack of intrinsic factor to which it binds. Taking in large quantities of liver would increase the amount of B_{12} ingested, since liver is a rich source, but would not help the underlying lack of intrinsic factor. Presumably enough would be absorbed directly, without the binding factor, to have some effect in alleviating the anaemia.

9.6.7 Pantothenic acid (vitamin B$_5$)

The name 'pantothenic acid' is derived from the Greek *pantothen* which means 'from all sides', indicating that it is widely distributed in the diet. It plays a vital role in metabolism, particularly in the production of energy in cells. Naturally occurring pantothenic acid deficiency is very rare, since it is so widespread in the diet. However, during World War II, prisoners in the Philippines, Burma and Japan suffering from severe malnutrition did experience numbness, tingling and painful burning in their feet, which was relieved specifically by pantothenic acid. In mice and rats, pantothenic acid deficiency led to their fur turning grey, and on the basis of this finding, pantothenic acid has been added to some shampoos, in the hope that it might prevent grey hair in humans. There is as yet no evidence that it does.

9.6.8 Biotin (vitamin H)

Although biotin is usually considered to be a member of the B vitamin complex, it is also sometimes known as vitamin H. Like pantothenic acid, it plays a major role in metabolism. Deficiency is not normally seen, though it can be induced in rats and people by feeding large quantities of raw egg white which binds biotin and prevents it being absorbed. Various symptoms result including hair loss, dermatitis, depression and lethargy.

9.7 Vitamin C (ascorbic acid)

● What is the condition that results from vitamin C deficiency and what are its symptoms?

◐ You should recall from the start of this study period that scurvy is the deficiency disease associated with lack of vitamin C and that its symptoms are loss of hair and teeth, bleeding gums, very slow healing of wounds and eventually death.

Vitamin C deficiency causes these symptoms because of its two important roles in the body. Firstly, it is used in the production of collagen (see SP4.6), which is found in large quantities in bone, tendons, cartilage and skin, and in smaller amounts in other tissues. And secondly, it is important in enhancing the absorption of iron (which is needed for red blood cells) from vegetable sources.

● Relate each of these roles of vitamin C to the symptoms of scurvy.

◐ The symptoms of scurvy can all be largely explained by failure of collagen production, including loss of teeth, which are held in place by connective tissue in the gums. Bleeding gums and very slow healing of other wounds are also caused by lack of collagen, which is needed to hold cells together, including the cells forming the blood vessels, but the poor healing may also be due to the lack of oxygen reaching the tissues due to shortage of iron in the blood (anaemia).

Although we tend to think of scurvy as a disease of sailors long ago, it does still occur in refugee camps where the diet contains insufficient vitamin C and among homeless people in the UK. Vitamin C is found in vegetables and fruit, especially blackcurrants and oranges. Potatoes are a good source too, though in the modern diet, more is probably obtained from fresh fruit and from fruit juices. Most mammals can synthesise their own vitamin C from glucose and so do not need it in their diet. However, along with humans and most other primates, guinea pigs lack this synthetic capacity. So some of the early research into vitamin C requirements was done in them, which is how 'guinea pig' came to mean a test subject in popular speech.

Vitamin C is very soluble in water. It is amongst the least stable of the vitamins and is rapidly destroyed by exposure to light and to air and by heating.

● Suggest three ways in which you could maximise the amount of vitamin C retained in cooked vegetables.

◉ You might have thought of some of the following: prepare the vegetables immediately before cooking, so exposing them to the air for the minimum time; cook them in the minimum amount of water (or steam them) for the minimum amount of time; keep the lid on the saucepan to prevent too much contact with the air; serve them immediately; use the cooking water in the meal if possible, since that may contain some of the vitamin C that has been leached out; and eat the vegetables immediately after cooking.

Vitamin C is readily absorbed from the digestive system and the total amount present in the body is typically about 2–3 g. Scurvy results when total body reserves fall below 300 mg. Vitamin C takes part in many of the body's metabolic processes and acts as an antioxidant (destroying free radicals). Vitamin C also appears to be beneficial to the immune system and there is evidence that moderate doses alleviate the symptoms of colds, though there is no convincing evidence that large doses can actually *prevent* colds. Many studies indicate that higher intake of vitamin C is linked with a lower risk of disease in general.

● Studies show that smokers have less vitamin C in their bodies than non-smokers. Why might this be?

◉ It may be because: (i) there is a lower intake – maybe the smoker has a cigarette after a meal, rather than a piece of fruit; (ii) there is poorer absorption in the gut; (iii) smoking generates more free radicals and the vitamin C is used up in destroying them.

Question SP9.5 Use Table SP9.1 to identify how much vitamin C is needed each day. If a person's diet contained no vitamin C, about how many days would it take for the level to fall low enough for symptoms of scurvy to appear? ◀

The following questions relate to the whole of SP9.

Question SP9.6 Use Table SP9.1 to identify which vitamins are likely to be lost (a) when a piece of frozen beef is defrosted and the water, some of which comes from inside the meat, is thrown away and (b) when fat drips from meat during the roasting process. ◀

Question SP9.7 (a) Which vitamins can be synthesised by cells in the body?

(b) Which vitamins are groups of compounds?

(c) Which three vitamins act as antioxidants? Are any of these synthesised in the body? ◀

Question SP9.8 Devise a table to show the similarities between the following pairs of vitamins: (a) riboflavin and niacin; (b) folate and vitamin B_{12}; (c) vitamins E and C.

Consider their sources, functions and signs of deficiency. ◀

Question SP9.9 A mother of three children under 5 is concerned that she is not giving them a balanced diet, since they mostly eat prepared convenience foods. What foods would you suggest that she introduces to their diet to boost their intake of vitamins? ◀

Activity SP9.1

Look through your file of articles, leaflets, etc. and re-read those that relate to vitamins. You should be able to understand them better now and judge the accuracy of the information in them. You could also look at labels on food packets, tins, etc., to see which have information about vitamins. Can you tell whether the food contains the vitamins naturally or whether they have been added by the manufacturer (fortified)?

Summary of SP9

1   Vitamins A, D, E and K are fat-soluble; the remainder are water-soluble.

2   Adequate amounts of vitamins are required, many on a regular basis, though some can be stored.

3   A balanced diet should provide the necessary amounts of vitamins, but people on a restricted diet need to take particular care to ensure an adequate intake of all of them.

4   Deficiency diseases can occur when vitamins are absent or in short supply.

5   Water-soluble vitamins are easily lost during cooking, and are destroyed by exposure to air and light, so care is needed in food preparation to preserve them.

Minerals, electrolytes and fluids

10.1 Introduction

Both vitamins and minerals are essential in the diet in small quantities and so they are often grouped together as micronutrients.

● Which items in the diet are classified as macronutrients?

● The macronutrients are proteins, fats and carbohydrates.

Minerals, also called mineral elements, are those elements other than carbon, hydrogen, oxygen and nitrogen, that are found in the body. These minerals are derived from the breakdown of the rocks of the Earth's crust which are then dissolved in water. So in a particular area, the minerals present in the local water depend on the underlying geology. Plants take up the water through their roots and, if those plants are used as food for people or animals, then the minerals enter their bodies. Animals are able to concentrate minerals in their tissues, so human foods of animal origin often contain a higher concentration than food obtained from plants. Minerals are also taken in through drinks. Minerals are needed in only small quantities in the diet, though some of them accumulate to a significant degree; for example, there is around 1 kg of calcium in the average human body. For most minerals, it is possible to identify their roles in the body, although some have, as yet, no known function.

10.2 Major minerals

The major mineral elements, defined here as those where 25 g or more is present in the body, are listed in Table SP10.1.

Table SP10.1 The major mineral elements required by the body. The recommended intakes (RNI) per day for a woman between the ages of 25 and 50 are listed. The approximate adult body content, functions and common food sources of the minerals are also shown.

Element (symbol)	RNI/g	Body content/g	Functions	Main food sources
calcium (Ca)	0.7	1000	major structural component of bones and teeth; necessary for many enzymes, including those of blood clotting, muscle contraction and conduction of nerve impulses	milk, cheese, bread and flour (if fortified), cereals, green vegetables
chlorine (Cl)	2.5	100	major negative ion (as chloride, Cl^-) in body fluids; present in stomach secretions as hydrochloric acid (HCl)	main source is salt (sodium chloride, NaCl) used in food processing, cooking, and at the table
magnesium (Mg)	0.3	25	present in bone, inside cells and in body fluids; needed for some enzymes	milk, bread and other cereal products, potatoes and other vegetables
phosphorus (P)	0.55	700	present in bones and teeth; essential for ATP and DNA and many other molecules	milk, cheese, bread and cereals, meat and meat products, nuts
potassium (K)	3.5	140	main positive ion inside cells; K^+ also present in extracellular fluids; essential for conduction of nerve impulses, also for the maintenance of ion concentration gradients across cell membranes	widely distributed in vegetables, meat, milk, fruit and fruit juices
sodium (Na)	1.6	100	major positive ion in extracellular fluids; Na^+ also present inside cells; essential for conduction of nerve impulses and active transport of small molecules across cell membranes (e.g. absorption from gut)	main source is salt (sodium chloride, NaCl) used in food processing, cooking, and at the table
sulfur (S)	no value set	150	present in proteins	protein-rich foods; meat, fish, eggs, milk, bread, cereals

Question SP10.1 You will see that Table SP10.1 is arranged with the elements in alphabetical order.

(a) If the table were to be arranged based on the recommended nutrient intake values, with the highest at the top, which two elements would appear at the top of the table?

(b) If, alternatively, the elements which occurred in the largest amounts in the body were to be at the top, which two elements would be at the top, and which one would appear at the bottom? ◀

10.2.1 Calcium (Ca)

About 40% of the total mineral mass of bones is calcium, making it the most abundant mineral in the body. In bone, it is combined with phosphorus, as well as oxygen and hydrogen, in a mineral compound called hydroxyapatite. Calcium is also present in the fluids in the body, and there it occurs in the form of dissolved ions.

● What is meant by an ion? You may need to look back to SP4.6.1.

◍ An ion is an atom that carries a very small electrical charge, which can be either positive (+) or negative (−), depending on the ion.

You may recall from SP9.2 that the charges are due to the loss or gain of electrons.

● A calcium ion is written as Ca^{2+}. What does this indicate in terms of the number of its electrons compared with an atom of calcium?

◍ A calcium atom must have lost 2 electrons to become Ca^{2+}, leaving it with two more protons in its nucleus than it has electrons around the outside, and thus an overall charge of +2.

Calcium ions, along with others, play an important role in the transmission of the electrical signals along the nerves of the body and in the brain, and in muscle contraction. Ions are also important in keeping the chemical composition constant inside cells and in the tissues around them. This process is one aspect of homeostasis, which is the maintenance of a stable internal environment in the body, by correcting any changes which occur to disturb that stable state. Calcium ions also play a role in blood clotting.

In the West, calcium is mainly obtained through milk and dairy products in the diet. Soya milk is usually enriched with calcium for vegetarians who do not consume dairy products. Calcium is present at a lower level in cereals and is added to most flour. It also occurs in green leafy vegetables and in those fish, like sardines, whose bones are eaten. Various compounds in food can bind to calcium and prevent it being released from the food so that it can be absorbed from the digestive system into the blood. For example, oxalates, which are present in spinach and rhubarb, may lock up the calcium in a compound called calcium oxalate. A meal containing these foods therefore provides the body with less calcium than would be expected. In general it appears that only about 30% of the calcium in food is actually absorbed into the blood; the rest is lost in the faeces.

● Which vitamin is involved in the uptake of calcium from the digestive system and what are the deficiency diseases associated with this vitamin in adults and children? Which other vitamin plays a part in the formation of bone?

◍ Vitamin D is involved in calcium uptake and the deficiency disease in adults is osteomalacia and in children, rickets (SP9.3). Vitamin K also has a role in bone formation (SP9.5).

With the natural ageing process, the amount of calcium present in the bones declines, especially in women for the first two to three years after the menopause. When this process has continued to the extent that the bones become fragile and easily broken, the condition is called osteoporosis. Inactivity and changes in some hormone levels, and certain drugs such as steroids, can increase the risk of osteoporosis. In 2000, there were 90 000 cases in the UK of fractures associated with osteoporosis, so it is a significant cause of illness (morbidity) and mortality in the population. The best method of prevention appears to be to achieve the maximum amount of bone mass (known as the peak bone mass, PBM) by the age of 20–25. Although bone composition is largely genetically controlled, various factors under the control of the individual can play an important role in teenagers and young adults, such as:

- Taking exercise. Increased muscle development leads to increased bone mass.
- Ensuring an adequate calcium intake, maybe as high as 1.3 g per day, i.e. significantly above the RNI value.
- Maintaining a normal BMI. Underweight female teenagers are particularly at risk, since a low BMI leads to lower bone mass. It also leads to amenorrhoea (ceasing of the normal menstrual cycle), when steroid hormones, such as oestrogen, are at lower levels than normal, and this also affects normal bone growth.
- Ensuring adequate vitamin D and K intake, as already mentioned.
- Vitamin C is important for collagen synthesis, and collagen forms part of the structural framework of bones, so adequate vitamin C intake is important too.
- Alcohol intake and cigarette smoking are linked with relatively lower bone mass.

In fact, many of these same factors apply to the maintenance of bone mass throughout life.

10.2.2 Phosphorus (P)

Like calcium, phosphorus is important in the structure of bones and teeth. It is vital in the body as part of the molecules ATP (SP8.3.3) and DNA (SP1.6) and is also a component of phospholipids (SP5.4.1), lipoproteins (SP5.4.3) and many other proteins too. Phosphorus can occur, combined with oxygen, in phosphate ions and in this form it plays an important role in switching on and off metabolic pathways in cells. Phosphorus is widely available in the diet, from both plant and animal sources, such as meat, fish, eggs and dairy products, cereals and nuts. It is also added to many prepared foods such as bread and cakes, processed meats and soft drinks. Since the body absorbs phosphorus more efficiently than calcium, intake is usually sufficient for the body's needs, but deficiency could lead to rickets and osteomalacia, as with calcium deficiency.

10.2.3 Magnesium (Mg)

Magnesium is also present in bone in the body and in the soft tissues, although in much lower quantities than calcium. It is important in the activity of more than 300 enzyme systems, in particular those using ATP. It is involved in the synthesis of proteins and in many other reactions in the body. In plants, magnesium is part of the chlorophyll molecule, so it is present in green vegetables and is found widely elsewhere in the diet, so intake is normally adequate. In some areas, there are low levels of magnesium in the drinking water, due to the lack of magnesium compounds in the underlying rocks. In such areas, surveys show that coronary heart disease is more common, though no clear causative link between magnesium and coronary heart disease has yet been found.

10.2.4 Sulfur (S)

Most proteins contain about 1% sulfur, which occurs in the side-chains (R groups) of two of the protein-forming amino acids. One is methionine.

● You have already met the other sulfur-containing amino acid. Look back to Table SP4.5 to find its name.

◑ The other sulfur-containing amino acid is cysteine.

Cysteine is particularly important in proteins such as collagen (found in bone, tendons, cartilage and skin) and keratin (found in hair and nails, as well as skin).

● What is the common feature of these two proteins that may be linked to the presence of cysteine in them?

◑ Collagen and keratin are both found in parts of the body that are relatively tough and strong. They are known as 'structural proteins'. Links between the sulfur atoms of the cysteines in adjacent protein (polypeptide) molecules link the molecules firmly together, providing that strength (for example, as shown in Figure SP4.8).

After injury, there is a particular need for sulfur to repair and build new structural proteins. However, a diet containing sufficient protein almost certainly provides sufficient sulfur for the body. Sulfur is also found in the vitamins biotin and thiamin and in some enzymes that play important roles in metabolism.

10.2.5 Sodium (Na), chlorine (Cl) and potassium (K)

The element sodium is a soft silvery metal and the element chlorine is a greenish gas that is poisonous to humans and many other animals. Yet when these two elements are combined together in a compound called sodium chloride, the properties are quite different. Sodium chloride in its solid form is composed of white crystals and we call it salt. When salt dissolves in water, the constituent sodium ions, Na^+, and chloride ions, Cl^-, become separated. Both of these ions are common in the body, sometimes to the extent that body fluids such as sweat taste quite salty. It is important to normal body functioning that the concentrations of sodium and chloride ions, together with potassium ions (K^+), in the blood and in the fluid around cells, are regulated within quite tight limits, however much or little is present in the diet. The ions are also essential for transmission of impulses along nerves and for muscle contraction.

● What is the name of the process by which the correct balance of ions is maintained within and around cells?

◑ It is called homeostasis (SP10.2.1).

In the UK, most people take in more sodium per day than is needed, mostly due to salt which is added to food either during the cooking process – particularly in manufactured foods, including bread – or at the table, to improve the taste of the food. There is no way of storing the ions and so the excess must be removed from the body by the kidneys in urine. It is particularly important that babies do not take in too much salt, since their kidneys are not fully developed and they are unable to remove excess from their bodies. If, when they start on solid food, they are given food with the normal adult quantity of salt, they can suffer kidney, liver and brain damage. As people get older, a small increase in salt intake has a greater effect on blood pressure than it does in younger people. The UK Government's guideline advice is that the intake of salt in adults should be no more than 5 g per day for women and 7 g for men. The average adult intake is currently around 9 g per day.

When levels of sodium are too high, the body retains too much water and the volume of body fluids increases, increasing the blood pressure (hypertension). High blood pressure is linked with a higher risk of cardiovascular disease and strokes. Reducing the salt intake does, over a number of weeks, lead to a blood pressure reduction. Since there appear to be no adverse consequences of a reduction in salt intake, such a reduction in the diet of all adults is to be recommended. However, this dietary change is not easy to achieve, since people become accustomed to the taste of a particular level of salt in food and taste buds need time to adapt to less. Additionally, food labels often give the sodium content of food, rather than the salt content.

- The mass of a chlorine atom is about one and a half times that of a sodium atom. Knowing that salt is made up of equal numbers of sodium and chorine atoms, how many times greater would the salt content of a food be than the sodium content?

- If you assume 1 unit for the mass of a sodium atom and 1.5 units for the mass of a chlorine atom, then the mass of sodium chloride is 2.5 units. So the salt content would be two and a half (2.5) times higher than the sodium content.

Question SP10.2 100 g of a particular breakfast cereal contains 0.3 g sodium while 100 g of a chicken curry ready-made meal contains 0.4 g sodium.

(a) Calculate the amount of salt present in 100 g of each of these foods.

(b) The average portion size of the cereal is 40 g while the ready-made meal, suitable for one person, is 450 g. How much salt would be taken in by eating a portion of each of them?

(c) How does this total amount compare with the advised daily salt intake for a woman? ◀

Like sodium ions and chloride ions, potassium ions are also widely distributed in foods and intakes are thought to be similar to those of sodium. However, potassium appears to have quite the opposite effect on blood pressure to sodium; the higher the potassium intake, the lower the blood pressure. Studies indicate that higher potassium levels allow the body to deal more effectively with excess sodium. Since fruit such as bananas, and vegetables, are good sources of potassium, more fruit and vegetables in the diet can have a beneficial effect on blood pressure.

10.3 Trace elements

The trace elements (also known as minor minerals or microminerals) are those that occur in quantities of less than about 5 g in the body. The more important ones are listed in Table SP10.2, though not all of them will be considered here.

Table SP10.2 Some trace elements needed by the human body. The functions and common food sources of the trace elements are shown.

Element (symbol)	Functions	Main food sources
chromium (Cr)	found in all tissues, may be involved in blood glucose regulation	liver, cereals, beer, yeast
cobalt (Co)	required for formation of red blood cells	liver and other meat
copper (Cu)	component of many enzymes; necessary for haemoglobin formation	green vegetables, fish, liver
fluorine (F)	prevents tooth decay	tea, seafood
iodine (I)	essential constituent of thyroid hormones	milk, seafood, iodised salt
iron (Fe)	essential component of haemoglobin in red blood cells	meat and offal, bread and flour, potatoes and other vegetables
manganese (Mn)	essential component of some enzymes	cereals, pulses, nuts
molybdenum (Mo)	essential component of some enzymes	kidney, cereals, vegetables, fruit
selenium (Se)	essential component of some enzymes; associated with vitamin E activity	cereals, meat, fish, eggs, Brazil nuts
zinc (Zn)	essential component of many enzymes and other proteins; required for steroid and thyroid hormone activity	meat and meat products, milk and cheese, bread flour and cereal products, peanuts, pulses

10.3.1 Fluorine (F)

Fluoride ions (F^-) are rare in foods, though some are found in tea and in seafood. However fluoride does occur naturally in some water supplies, derived from the rocks through which the water flows. Its only role in the body appears to be to help to protect teeth from decay.

● Look back to SP6.10 and list, as a series of bullet points, the stages of tooth decay.

- The stages are as follows:
  - bacteria live in saliva on teeth (form plaque)
  - produce lactic acid → dissolves calcium salts in tooth enamel
  - produce protein-digesting enzymes → destroy enamel protein
  - eventually enamel surface of tooth is breached
  - underlying softer dentine is attacked
  - cavities form in the teeth.

- The main structural chemical in the enamel of teeth is the same as that in bone. Look back to SP10.2.1 to identify the chemical and its important component elements.

- It is called hydroxyapatite, and contains the minerals calcium and phosphorus, as well as oxygen and hydrogen.

Acid dissolves the hydroxyapatite, a process called demineralisation. Once the acid has been neutralised by the saliva, the minerals can be restored to the tooth surface in a process called remineralisation. However, too many sugary foods mean that there is insufficient time for this remineralisation to occur completely and the tooth begins to decay. It is thought that fluoride helps to prevent this decay in several different ways:

1 As the enamel is developing in children's teeth, if fluoride is present, it replaces the OH (hydroxy-) part of hydroxyapatite, forming fluoroapatite, which is harder and more resistant to decay.

2 When the remineralisation process is occurring in the presence of fluoride, again the newly formed enamel is stronger.

3 Fluoride becomes concentrated inside the plaque bacteria, which reduces their ability to produce acid, so less demineralisation of the teeth occurs.

4 There is some evidence that children who grow up in areas where fluoride is present in the water have shallower grooves in the biting surfaces of their teeth, thus reducing the places where bacteria can lodge to form plaque.

It seems likely that the remineralisation effect (2) is the most important and so the control of sugars in the diet and the regular use of fluoride toothpaste, to supplement fluoride in the water, are the best preventative measures.

For the protection of teeth, the optimal level of fluoride in drinking water is 1 gram of fluoride per million grams of water (abbreviated to 1 part per million or 1 p.p.m.). In areas where fluoride levels are naturally low, this mineral can be added to the water supply, as it is in some areas of the UK. However, there is some controversy about this measure due to concerns that fluoride could be in some way harmful to health, although there is no scientific evidence to support that claim. The only adverse effect of fluoride appears to be that when fluoride intake is too high, children's teeth can become mottled with opaque white patches (dental fluorosis). The teeth remain functionally normal and resistant to decay and only their appearance is affected.

10.3.2 Iodine (I)

Iodide ions (I⁻) derived, like all mineral elements, from the breakdown of rocks, is present in some soils, but much of it has been dissolved out by water over millions of years and washed down into the sea. It is concentrated by some marine organisms, and so can occur at quite high concentrations in edible seaweed, and in fish and other seafood. Thus people living near coasts often have sufficient iodine in their diet, whereas those living in mountainous areas, such as the Himalayas and Andes, where most of the iodine has been removed from the soil by millennia of high rain and snowfall, can suffer from iodine deficiency.

Figure SP10.1 The condition of goitre where the thyroid gland enlarges due to an inadequate intake of iodine.

Iodine is an essential component of thyroid hormones, produced by the thyroid gland at the base of the neck. These hormones play a vital part in the regulation of metabolic processes, especially growth and energy expenditure. If there is insufficient iodine for the production of normal amounts of these hormones, the thyroid gland enlarges as the cells attempt to boost their hormone production. Ultimately, the swollen thyroid produces an enlargement of the throat called a goitre (Figure SP10.1). Not only does the swelling impede breathing and swallowing, but the lack of sufficient thyroid hormones also leads to weight gain, lethargy, intolerance to cold, increased blood cholesterol, mental slowness and reduced heart function.

Iodine deficiency has its greatest impact during pregnancy, since it has major effects on the developing brain and physical growth of the fetus. In the worst case, the child suffers from cretinism, in which there is mental retardation, stunted growth, apathy, and impairment of movement, speech and hearing. However, even minor iodine deficiency can lower a child's IQ by between 10 and 15 points, which, if it occurs in a large percentage of the population, can severely hamper the economic development of a country. Iodine deficiency is regarded as the greatest cause of preventable brain damage, putting almost a thousand million children at risk worldwide. A UN initiative aims to eliminate the problem by adding iodine to salt, since salt is consumed by almost everyone in the world, regardless of culture or socioeconomic group. In the UK, cows' milk is a major source of iodine due to the use of iodine-containing supplements in cattle food.

Nuclear accidents can release radioactive isotopes of iodine into the environment, which can then contaminate water and food supplies. The iodine settles onto the grass in pasture land, and is then eaten by cattle, and appears in their milk – a major way in which it is taken in by people. Radioactive iodine can become concentrated in the thyroid gland and cause thyroid cancers. If a large amount of normal (non-radioactive) iodine is taken in, it can displace the radioactive iodine (which is then excreted) and reduce the chances of cancer developing. This non-toxic iodine can be supplied to those at risk in the form of potassium iodide tablets. After the explosion at the nuclear power plant at Chernobyl in 1986, such tablets were supplied to 10.5 million adults and 7 million children thought to be at risk.

10.3.3 Iron (Fe)

The ability of blood to carry oxygen is due to the presence of the red pigment, haemoglobin, present in red blood cells (see SP1.7). Haemoglobin is a protein formed from four polypeptide chains called globins, in the centre of each of which is a small non-protein part called a haem group (*haima* is Greek for 'blood'). Each of the haem groups has an iron atom within it (Figure SP10.2).

oxygen-binding site
(haem group)

Figure SP10.2 Schematic diagram showing the structure of the haemoglobin molecule, with four globin chains and a haem group within each.

The majority of iron in the body is in the form of haemoglobin. The total amount present depends on a number of factors, including gender and body weight, as well as general health.

Question SP10.3 (a) If a woman weighing 60 kg has 40 mg of iron for each kilogram of body weight (mass), how much iron will her body contain?

(b) If two-thirds of the iron in the body is contained in haemoglobin molecules, how many grams of iron will be in the woman's haemoglobin? ◀

Iron is also found in another molecule, that also binds to oxygen, called myoglobin (see Figure SP4.6). A myoglobin molecule is very similar to a quarter of a haemoglobin molecule, i.e. one globin chain with its associated haem. The red colour in the meat that we eat (the muscles of animals) is due to myoglobin. There are several types of fibres in muscles, including red fibres and white fibres, and whether the meat has a light or dark colour depends on the amount of each type present. Red muscle fibres predominate in those muscles that sustain long periods of activity. Fat may be stored around these muscles as an energy source, and the oxygen needed to combine with the fat to provide energy when the muscles are active is obtained from myoglobin. The myoglobin constantly replenishes its oxygen by picking it up from the haemoglobin in the blood. So these muscle fibres are high in myoglobin, which gives them their red colour. White fibres are found in muscles that are only required to be active for a short time. They use glucose from the blood as an energy source (or stored glycogen, see SP6.5.3), and so there is little fat around the muscles. Less oxygen is needed to combine with glucose, and so less myoglobin is present and the muscles are lighter in colour.

● Where do you find red meat and white meat in a cooked chicken? Can you relate this distribution to the requirement for myoglobin?

- Chickens have red meat on the legs and white meat on the breast. Since the legs are used almost continuously for standing and walking, you would expect more myoglobin to be present and therefore the meat would be red. The breast muscles are used for flight and, since flights are rare and short in chickens, the myoglobin levels are low and so the breast meat is much paler. In birds that fly more, such as wild ducks, the breast meat is much darker in colour.

Liver is another type of meat that is very rich in iron, since the liver is where all mammals, including ourselves, store their iron, bound to a protein called ferritin. Cereals contain iron, though it is usually bound to a substance called phytate which is also found in nuts and some vegetables, and which also binds to calcium and zinc. Being bound in this way means that the iron from vegetables and cereals is less easily absorbed than the iron from animal products. However, phytate is removed by milling and then white bread flour is fortified with iron to ensure that bread is a useful source of the mineral. Various other substances in the diet can also bind iron and therefore prevent its absorption, while others, including vitamin C, can enhance the amount that is absorbed. The complex interaction with other foods makes it extremely difficult to predict just how much iron will be absorbed into the body from a particular meal. The average amount of iron in the diet is about the same as the RNI, which hides the fact that many individuals, especially women, are deficient in iron.

- Can you recall, from SP1.7, what is missing in red blood cells that is present in almost all other cells in the body?

- Red blood cells do not have a nucleus and so, without a set of chromosomes, they are unable to make new components or repair any damage.

Since red blood cells spend a lot of their time being squeezed through tiny blood capillaries, often not much wider than themselves, they are easily damaged and this results in their limited lifespan of about 120 days. So, there is a huge daily turnover of red blood cells. In fact, every second, one and a half million (1 500 000) red blood cells are destroyed, and the same number of new ones are produced. If the iron was not recycled from the red cells that are destroyed, 240 mg of iron would be needed every day. Red cells are broken down mostly in the liver (and spleen), where the iron is stored attached to ferritin, as mentioned earlier, and new red cells are made in the bone marrow. So there is a requirement for iron to be transported in the blood between these sites, which it does attached to a protein called transferrin. Small amounts of the storage protein, ferritin, are present in the blood and a fall in ferritin level is the first sign of iron deficiency. If the deficiency persists, the red cells that are produced are smaller and contain less haemoglobin than normal and gradually the person develops the symptoms of anaemia, with tiredness and lack of appetite. It is thought that anaemia may affect one-tenth of the world population. A change in diet or taking iron supplements should correct the condition.

10.3.4 Selenium (Se)

Selenium is found in the body in an important group of enzymes (glutathione peroxidases) which have important antioxidant properties and work in conjunction with vitamins C and E to destroy free radicals in cells. Some studies have shown that a higher selenium level is linked to a lower risk of breast, prostate and colon cancer, which may in part be due to selenium's antioxidant function. Other selenium-containing proteins help to regulate thyroid function and play a role in the immune system.

The selenium content of foods depends partly on the protein level, since selenium is found attached to the amino acid cysteine in animal proteins and to methionine in plant proteins. However, the level in food also depends on the selenium content of the soil where the plants are grown or the animals are raised. Levels are low where soils are acid and there is heavy rainfall. Soils in some parts of China and Russia have very low amounts of selenium and selenium deficiency is often reported in those regions because most food in those areas is grown and eaten locally. Selenium is found in fish, meat and eggs and in bread, though the level depends on the source of the wheat. Much of the wheat from America and Canada contains sufficient selenium, but when bread-makers in the UK switched from Canadian to European wheat, the selenium levels in the wheat were found to be 10 to 50 times lower, resulting in a significant fall in the daily intake of selenium in the UK. At least one bread manufacturer subsequently added selenium to their products. An alternative solution is to encourage farmers to use fertilizer containing added selenium, on their land. In the UK, Brazil nuts are the richest dietary source of selenium and if eaten in large quantities, could result in excess intake.

Selenium deficiency may contribute to the development of arthritis, coronary heart disease, thyroid malfunction, and to a weakened immune system. Evidence suggests that selenium deficiency does not usually cause illness by itself, but makes the body more susceptible to illnesses caused by other nutritional, biochemical or infectious stresses. Keshan Disease, named after the area of China where it was originally found, is a specific disease associated with selenium deficiency, resulting in an enlarged heart and poor heart function in children. It was first described in the early 1930s, though now has largely been eliminated due to a more varied intake of food.

10.3.5 Zinc (Zn)

Zinc is involved in many metabolic processes in the body, due to its importance in the functioning of more than 100 enzymes. These control, amongst other things, metabolism of foods, production of energy, cell division and protein synthesis. The body contains 2 to 3 g of zinc in total. Zinc is most commonly found in protein-rich foods, such as meat, and also in peanuts and pulses (peas and beans). Generally sufficient is available in Western diets, although there is some concern that amounts are declining due to increased processing of food and there may be insufficient reserves in some individuals to cope with increasing demands such as during periods of increased growth in children, during pregnancy and during wound healing after injury. Vegetarians who consume a variety of legumes and nuts will probably take in sufficient zinc, but other vegetarian diets may not contain enough, especially since zinc from plant sources is absorbed less readily than that from animal foods.

The clearest evidence of zinc deficiency was seen in the 1960s, when Iranian military officials noted that an unusual number of young men eligible for army duty were short in stature and showed delayed sexual maturation, as well as a number of other symptoms. Earlier research had shown that similar symptoms developed in animals if they were deprived of zinc in the diet. When the zinc levels of the army recruits were tested, they were found to be particularly low. Their normal diet was based almost exclusively on cereals, which although they do contain zinc, also contain chemicals called phytates (see SP10.3.3) which prevent the zinc from being absorbed. Furthermore, many of the young men indulged in the strange habit of geophagia, or clay eating. Clay binds to zinc in the digestive system and slows down its absorption. After treatment with a well-balanced diet containing adequate amounts of zinc for a year, pubic hair appeared, sexual organs increased in size, and growth in height was resumed, so confirming the vital role of zinc.

Signs of mild zinc deficiency are less dramatic and there is no specific deficiency disease associated with zinc. Instead many general signs appear such as poor appetite, a decrease in the sense of taste and smell, weight loss, poor night vision, delayed healing of wounds and repeated infections. About 25% of people who have an impairment in taste and or smell are suffering from zinc deficiency. Half of people with anorexia nervosa also appear to have a zinc deficiency and there is some evidence that zinc supplements improve the condition. Zinc supplements are sometimes used to treat skin ulcers or bed sores, but they do not increase rates of wound healing when zinc levels are normal. Zinc and castor oil creams are used to prevent nappy rash in babies. There are also health risks if the intake of zinc is too high. Metal fume fever, also called brass-founders' ague or zinc shakes, is an industrial disease caused by inhaling zinc oxide fumes, which cause damage to the nervous system.

10.4 Fluid balance

Although a person can survive for several weeks without food, without fluids, someone can survive for only a few days. A loss of water equivalent to just 1% of body weight is enough to make someone feel thirsty and to have an effect on ability to concentrate. Such a loss has been shown in some studies in schools to result in a 10% decrease in the mental performance of children. A 4% loss results in dizziness and reduced muscle power. By the time there is a 6% loss, the heart is racing and sweating ceases and a 7% loss results in collapse and subsequent death, if the loss is not replaced.

10.4.1 Fluid loss

During an average day, a person in a temperate climate such as the UK, loses about 2.5 litres of water.

● How is water lost from the body?

◑ The main loss is through the production of urine. Some water is lost through the skin as sweat and some in the faeces. Water is also lost from the lungs in breathing; you know that breathing out onto a cold glass surface produces condensation and in cold weather, the water vapour in the breath condenses into visible droplets in the air.

Urine output is controlled by the kidneys and even in cases of quite severe dehydration, urine production continues, since it is needed to rid the body of the nitrogen-containing compound, urea, which is produced as a result of the breakdown of amino acids from proteins (SP4.7.2). In a dehydrated person, the output of urine can be as low as 0.5 litres per day and it will be a dark brown colour. A more normal output is 1.5 litres and a light yellow colour indicates that the body is well hydrated. Sweating is part of the system that regulates the body temperature. Heat from the body is used to evaporate sweat from the surface of the skin and so the evaporation has a cooling effect. A typical loss of water through sweating of about 0.5 litres per day can increase in hot weather and during exercise to up to 2 litres per *hour*. The losses from the lungs (0.4 litres daily) and in faeces (0.1 litres daily) are normally fairly constant. However, diarrhoea increases the loss from the digestive tract hugely and can quickly result in dangerous levels of dehydration if the fluid is not replaced. Diarrhoeal diseases are common where people live in overcrowded conditions without a clean water supply, and there are an estimated 10 million cases and 5000 deaths each day throughout the world. Since both water and ions are lost, the best treatment for diarrhoea is oral rehydration, using sachets of commercially prepared rehydration mixture or a home-made solution containing eight teaspoons of sugar (to provide energy and to mask the taste of the salt) and one teaspoon of salt in a litre of water, together with some mashed banana or orange juice if available.

● In addition to water, what are the main mineral ions present in this home-made rehydration solution?

◐ Salt is sodium chloride, so the solution will contain sodium ions and chloride ions. Bananas and orange juice are good sources of potassium ions. All three ions are vital for the normal functioning of the body.

10.4.2 Fluid gain

In a normal diet, fluid is gained via food as well as in drinks. The amount of water in various foods is shown in Table SP10.3. As well as plain water, most drinks, such as tea, coffee, juices and milk drinks, hydrate the body, but alcoholic drinks may not. Alcohol is a diuretic, a substance that increases the output of urine by the body. Calculations indicate that for each unit of alcohol taken in (1 unit = about 8 g alcohol), about 80 ml of extra water is lost from the body. If the unit of alcohol is taken in as a half pint of beer, then more fluid would have been taken in than was lost, so dehydration would not result. However, if the alcohol is taken in as wine or spirits, in a much smaller volume, then dehydration can result. Advice to alternate alcoholic and soft drinks, and to drink extra water at bedtime, is designed to offset the dehydration effect and go some way towards preventing a 'hangover' the next day. Caffeine, found in coffee and tea, is also a diuretic but over 300 mg a day is needed to have a diuretic effect and surveys in the UK find daily intakes well below this value. Individual fluid requirements vary but intakes of about 1 litre per day in food and 1.5 litres in drinks (non-alcoholic) are typical.

● Water is also produced in the body. Which processes have been described earlier that produce water?

Table SP10.3 The water content of some foods.

Food	Water/%
lettuce	95
carrots	90
boiled potatoes	80
grapes	80
lentil soup	78
grilled oily fish	65
cooked meat	60
potato chips	52
white bread	37
Cheddar cheese	36
cake	15
cornflakes	3
semi-sweet biscuits	2.5

● When proteins are synthesised by linking together amino acids, a water molecule is produced for every peptide bond made (Figure SP4.4). When fatty acids are joined to glycerol to make a fat (triacylglycerol), water molecules are also generated (Figure SP5.2). And finally, linking monosaccharides together to make carbohydrates also generates water (Figure SP6.5). Overall, about a quarter of a litre (0.25 litre) of water per day is gained by the body from such metabolic processes.

Many people now drink mineral water, often carrying a bottle with them. Mineral water is thought to be 'better' in some way than drinking tapwater. In fact, tapwater contains adequate minerals too. Currently in the UK, water companies must satisfy the requirements of the Water Supply (Water Quality) Regulations 1989, which give prescribed concentration values (upper limits) for 57 different parameters. The limits for a few of them are given in Table SP10.4.

The regulations also specify a range for the pH of 5.5–5.9 for tapwater. pH is a measure of the acidity or alkalinity of the water, with 7 being neutral, values below 7 being acidic and those above 7 being alkaline. The dry residue is the amount of material left when a sample of the water is boiled to dryness.

Question SP10.4 Compare the values in Table SP10.4 with those from the label on a bottle of 'Carbonated natural mineral water' (Figure SP10.3). Comment on the comparisons. ◀

Carbonated Natural Mineral Water

Typical analysis	mg per litre
Calcium	25.6
Magnesium	6.4
Potassium	<1.0
Sodium	6.4
Bicarbonate	98.3
Sulphate	10.1
Nitrate	<2.5
Fluoride	<0.1
Chloride	6.8
Silicate	7.6
Dry residue at 180°C	109.1
pH	4.6

Figure SP10.3 Part of the label from a bottle of mineral water.

Table SP10.4 The legal upper limits of some dissolved mineral ions in drinking water in the UK.

	Upper limits/ mg per litre
calcium (Ca^{2+})	250
magnesium (Mg^{2+})	50
potassium (K^+)	12
sodium (Na^+)	150
chloride (Cl^-)	400
sulphate (SO_4^{2-})	250
nitrate (NO_3^-)	50
dry residue	1500

Tapwater and mineral water may, of course, come from exactly the same source. However, some tapwater is obtained from sources that are at risk of contamination from microbes, and in the UK, tapwater is therefore filtered and pretreated with chlorine and other chemicals to make it safe to drink. Bottled water that is labelled as 'Natural mineral water' is extracted from the ground, and is bottled at source without any treatment. If the water is sparkling when it comes from the ground it is labelled as 'Naturally carbonated natural mineral water'. If the carbon dioxide is added at the bottling plant, it must be labelled 'Carbonated (or sparkling) natural mineral water'. Water labelled as 'Spring water' must be obtained from an underground source, be bottled at source and be micro-biologically safe without any treatment. However, certain other treatments, such as the chemical removal of minerals whose levels are too high, are permitted. 'Table water', on the other hand, need comply only with regulations on water quality for tapwater and can be bottled anywhere.

Summary of SP10

1   Certain minerals are required in the body.

2   Some minerals form essential structural components of tissues. For example, calcium, phosphorus and magnesium compounds are major components of bones and teeth. Fluoride is also important in protecting teeth from decay.

3   Sodium, potassium, calcium and chloride ions are important in maintaining the correct composition of cells and of the tissue fluids around them (homeostasis). These same ions are also involved in communication between cells, in particular the rapid transfer of signals along nerve cells and in the brain. They also play a part in muscle contraction.

4   Some minerals are essential components of important molecules such as hormones and enzymes. For example, the hormones produced by the thyroid gland contain iodine and many enzymes need magnesium, selenium or zinc to function. Sulfur is an essential component of some amino acids and iron is incorporated into haemoglobin and related proteins.

5   The correct fluid balance is also essential for normal functioning of the body.

6   Tapwater, and not just mineral water, contains minerals.

Pregnancy and lactation

For the remaining study periods, you will be working again with the book *Extracts from Human Nutrition* (referred to as HN), applying your understanding and the study skills you have developed in Parts One and Two, to the links between nutrition and health for people of all ages and a range of lifestyles. This Study Book acts as a guide to your study of each HN chapter, with some background information where necessary. The frequent numbered questions are designed to help consolidate your learning and give you practice for the course assessment, so it is important to try writing answers to all of them yourself before checking our version.

11.1 Introduction

You will find that HN Chapter 11 contains a lot of detailed human biology. For the purposes of the course, you do not need to understand these details and provided that you can answer the questions here, you will have achieved the course learning outcomes.

If new words and concepts that you find in the text and in the diagrams in HN Part Three are not in an ordinary dictionary or in the *Course Glossary*, then you need not spend time looking them up elsewhere.

When dealing with unfamiliar material, scientists regularly find themselves in the situation of reading scientific information some of which they do not understand. If you have tried to access any of the papers from scientific journals, listed at the ends of the HN chapters, you will probably already have encountered the problem. Even experienced scientists find such papers hard to follow if they are describing work in an unfamiliar area. It is best to learn to read past the words that you do not understand in order to get the general gist of the material and just accept that time does not allow you to understand all the details. It is quite a difficult skill, so you will probably need some practice before you feel that it is not causing you problems. The important point to bear in mind is that as long as you can answer the questions set here, you will have gained what is required for this course from the HN chapter.

Now would be a good time to think about your study techniques so far. When you were studying HN Part One, did you find it useful to read through the chapters in short sections, answering the questions as you went along, or did you prefer to read the whole of a chapter and then deal with all the questions at the end? Did you make notes or did you highlight important words? How did you deal with unfamiliar words? Did your study technique change for Part Two? Consider the answers to these questions and decide how it will be best for you to study this final part of the course.

11.2 Early pregnancy

Read from the start of HN Chapter 11 on p. 231 as far as the bottom of the first column on p. 234.

Now think back over how you dealt with unfamiliar words in this section. You may have needed to look up 'perinatal' and 'neonatal' in an ordinary dictionary; you should have found 'retinol' and 'neural tube defects' in the *Glossary*. Retinol is mentioned briefly in SP9.2 as a form of vitamin A and neural tube defects in SP9.6.5 in the section on folate. This HN section includes the terms 'teratogenic' and 'antimutagenic'.

● What do you understand by the term teratogenic?

◍ A teratogenic substance is defined on HN p. 233 as one that can cause fetal malformations, so a teratogenic substance could result in abnormalities in the baby (though they may not become apparent until later life).

Normally the word is used to mean abnormalities that are not inherited, so that the baby, when it grew up, would not pass on the abnormalities to its own children. However, there are also abnormal changes that can occur in the genes of the egg or sperm or very early embryo. These changes are called mutations and the problems that they cause would then be passed on to future generations. Some mutations occur spontaneously; others are caused by such factors as radiation (including X-rays) and certain chemicals, known as mutagens. An antimutagenic substance is one that prevents such genetic changes.

Question SP11.1 A friend has confided that she is hoping to start a pregnancy within the next few months. Summarise the nutritional advice that you would give her from now until the pregnancy is confirmed by her doctor after about the first 6 weeks. Try to answer this question in 200–250 words. You may find it useful to re-read the advice about writing accounts like this that was given at the end of SP6. ◀

11.3 Pregnancy

Read from HN p. 234 'Nutrition during pregnancy' to the end of the section 'Who is most at risk in pregnancy?' towards the end of p. 240.

Question SP11.2 Read the 'Diet tips for pregnancy' summary in HN Figure 11.3 p. 237.

(a) Using the information about vitamins in SP9, including Table SP9.1, comment on the accuracy of the item of advice in that list that reads 'Increase fruit & vegetable intake to provide vitamins A & C, riboflavin, folate & vitamin D'. Consider each vitamin in turn.

(b) What is the basis for the advice that 'If pregnant through the winter, may need to take vitamin D supplements'? ◀

Now read from the bottom of HN p. 240 'Long-term consequences of intrauterine events' to half way down the first column of p. 245. *You will probably find all of the section quite difficult and you do not need to understand it in detail.*

● What do you understand by the phrase 'negative correlation' (HN p. 241, second column)?

● If there is a negative correlation between two measurements, it means that as one goes up, the other goes down. 'Negative association' and 'reciprocal relationship' mean the same. So, a 'negative correlation between weight at birth and the incidence of coronary heart disease later in life' means that as birth weight goes up, CHD incidence appears to go down. Or, put another way, adults who were small at birth are believed to be more likely to suffer from CHD than adults who were large babies.

Question SP11.3 Describe in your own words, in one or two sentences, what is meant by 'programming' (near the top of p. 241) in the context of fetal development. ◀

Question SP11.4 Make a list of the major conditions that are linked with low birthweight. (You do not need to understand the complexity of the details of the links as shown in HN Figure 11.4 p. 244.) ◀

11.4 Lactation

Read from HN p. 245 'The nursing or lactating mother' to the end of the chapter on p. 249.

Question SP11.5 Describe, in about 150 words, the control of the processes of milk production and milk ejection, and the composition of human milk, as summarised in HN Figure 11.5 p. 246. ◀

Question SP11.6 The following questions are based on the information in HN Table 11.4 (p. 247).

(a) Identify which aspects of a new mother's nutritional intake should be increased when she begins to breastfeed her baby, if her diet was in line with the dietary reference values towards the end of her pregnancy.

(b) Which of the vitamins and minerals could be obtained if the mother simply increased the amount of cows' milk that she was drinking each day. You will need to look back at Table SP9.1 and relevant sections of SP10.

(c) Suggest foods that she might eat to obtain easily those vitamins and minerals not in the cows' milk.

(d) Why would she probably not require an additional intake of iron? ◀

Summary of SP11

1   The nutrition of a mother is particularly important prior to conception and during the first few weeks of pregnancy. Increased levels of folate (folic acid) can help to prevent neural tube defects. Alcohol can be teratogenic.

2   During pregnancy, the mother's body can adapt to varying intakes of energy, though women who have lower energy and nutrient intakes during pregnancy give birth to smaller babies.

3   Extra nutrients are advisable during the last three months of pregnancy.

4   Low birth weight appears to be negatively correlated with some aspects of health in later life.

5   Lactation produces additional demands on the mother's body, requiring increased intake of some nutrients and water.

STUDY PERIOD 12

Infants, children and adolescents

12.1 Introduction

Read the introductory section of HN Chapter 12 on p. 251.

● Make a list of the reasons why diet in children is so important.

◌ Childhood diet is important because:

- It keeps the child healthy and allows normal growth, development and function.
- It can overcome some of the problems that result from being born exceptionally small.
- It can prevent the child from becoming overweight.
- It can ensure adequate intakes of calcium to promote bone growth, and appropriate intakes of other vitamins and minerals.

All these factors can influence health in later life.

12.2 Infants

Read the HN section 'Infants' pp. 251–257, but omit both the section on Growth on p. 252 and Figure 12.1 on p. 253. Ignore the detailed information on the manufacture of infant milk from cows' milk on p. 252.

● Identify two occasions on p. 254 where the text mentions 'antibodies'. Do you get the impression that antibodies are beneficial or not?

◌ The first mention indicates that antibodies are useful. They are present in maternal milk (or in colostrum – the first secretion from the breast after giving birth, before the true 'milk' is produced). The second mention is rather negative, in that proteins that are absorbed by babies from eggs or cows' milk may generate antibodies and cause allergies in future.

The immune system is a complex of cells and molecules in the body, that normally helps to fight off disease. When disease-causing bacteria or viruses enter the body, one of the body's reactions is to produce antibodies to them, that help in the process of destroying them and therefore allow recovery from the infection. The antibodies remain in the bloodstream and can prevent future infections by the same organism. Vaccinations given to individuals, usually by injection, introduce antibodies into the body and so prevent the disease directly. Alternatively, they may contain inactive versions of the disease-causing organism, so that the body generates its own antibodies and can therefore be ready to fight off a future infection by that organism. As stated on p. 254, antibodies made by the mother are contained in her milk, and so can be passed on to her baby to help to give some protection against infection in the early weeks or months. However, if the baby is given cows' milk or eggs when it is too young and its immune system is still developing, it is possible for the baby to produce antibodies inappropriately against the proteins contained in them. These antibodies can then react against milk and eggs in the diet later, so that the child becomes allergic to them. So the generally beneficial immune system can also cause health problems.

Check your understanding of pp. 251–257 by answering the following questions.

Question SP12.1 (a) Write a few sentences explaining the different way in which proteins are digested and absorbed in infants compared with that in adults, and the effect of these differences. (You may find it helpful to re-read SP4.7.)

(b) Why is the amount of protein in the infant diet especially important? You should consider the effect of both insufficient and excess protein. ◀

> In Question SP12.1, you were referred back to the specific section in SP4 where you could revise information on protein digestion and it would be possible to add similar hints to many of the questions that follow. However, by this stage of the course you should be able to find these sections yourself, using your notes or the index of this Study Book and so such references will generally be omitted from now on.

Question SP12.2 HN Table 12.2 p. 255 gives the estimated average requirements for energy for children up to the age of 12 months. Study it carefully, making sure that you understand the headings of each of the columns and that you recall the units in which energy is measured.

(a) What is the energy requirement in kilocalories (Calories) for a baby girl aged 8 months and weighing 8 kg?

(b) Why do boys have a greater EAR than girls? Hint: Look at the relationship between the 'Average weight', 'Requirement' and 'EAR' columns.

(c) Look back to Table SP7.2 and calculate how many kcal per kg you need each day, based on your age and your weight in kg. Comment on the difference between this value and the value for a 6-month-old baby boy. ◀

Question SP12.3 HN p. 255 states that 'long-chain *n*-3 [fatty] acids are important for development of the brain, vascular systems [blood systems] and retina [in the eye]'. What is meant by a long-chain *n*-3 fatty acid? Give the names of two *n*-3 fatty acids. ◀

Question SP12.4 Human milk contains lactose, although 'infants can also digest and utilize sucrose' (HN p. 256). How are these sugars similar and what is the difference in their chemical composition? ◀

Question SP12.5 'Breastfed infants are also at risk of low vitamin K intakes' (HN p. 256). What is a possible consequence of low vitamin K in newborn babies? ◀

Now read quickly through the section 'Breastfeeding or bottle-feeding?' in HN pp. 257–260. There is no need to make notes on any of this section. The social classes referred to on p. 257 are explained on p. 311. After reading this section, you should have a general appreciation of the complexities in manufacturing formula milks for infants to make them as close as possible in composition to breast milk, but you do not need to understand any of the details.

12.3 Weaning and nutrition to age five

Read HN pp. 260–265 up to 'School-age children'. Near the start of p. 264, you will read the phrase 'non-milk extrinsic sugars'. Sugar in the diet can be categorised into intrinsic and extrinsic sugars. Intrinsic sugars are those that are present within plant cells, such as those of fruit. They are thought to have little or no adverse impact on health. Extrinsic sugars are those sugars that are added to food and they do have adverse effects, such as playing a major part in tooth decay (dental caries). Although the sugar in milk (lactose) is technically an extrinsic sugar, since it is found outside cells, it is a naturally occurring sugar and is usually considered in the diet to be more similar to intrinsic sugars. Hence, 'non-milk extrinsic sugars' is the phrase that is often used to indicate those sugars that are added to foods.

● What do you understand by the phrase in the third bullet point on p. 265, 'There was a reciprocal relationship between fat and sugar intakes'?

◗ A reciprocal relationship is one in which one factor goes up as the other goes down (SP11.3). So here, it refers to the finding that those children who had a high dietary fat intake, had a low sugar intake, and those with a high sugar intake had a low fat intake.

● In the fifth bullet point of the same list, it is stated that 24% of children aged from one and a half to two and a half years old had iron intakes below the LRNI. In a random sample of 200 children in this age group, how many would be short of iron?

◗ The LRNI value is set such that only 2.5% of the population needs less than that value (HN pp. 42–43). So in a random sample of 200 children, it would be expected that only 5 (2.5% of 200) would *need* less than the LRNI value. The survey shows that 48 children in this group have iron levels below the LRNI value (24% of 200). So, out of every 200 children, 43 children (48 – 5) would be short of iron.

Question SP12.6 A 9-month-old child eats cereal at breakfast time, with skimmed milk, a soft cheese spread on rusks or bread at lunchtime and has a jar of baby-food in the evening, followed by a small piece of cake. She usually drinks a sweetened orange drink in her bottle. Her mother is determined not to give any additional vitamin supplements to her child. Use the information from this section of HN, and from SP9, to compile a list of five points of advice that you would give to the mother about her child's diet, with a brief scientific explanation of your advice. ◀

12.4 School-age children

Read the section on 'School-age children' from HN pp. 265–273. HN Table 12.6 p. 268 is particularly important as it gives the general dietary guidelines for adults for the intakes of fat and carbohydrates.

Question SP12.7 Answer (a)–(c) below, in 50–100 words for each part.

(a) What are the main nutritional guidelines underlying the balance of a diet suitable for children aged between 5 and 10?

(b) What problems might be encountered in adhering to these guidelines?

(c) Which nutrients might be most at risk? ◀

> You will notice that the answers to Question SP12.7 contain references to the page(s) in HN from which the information has been obtained. Referencing the source of information in this way is an important skill in scientific writing, so that others can go back to the original source to confirm what you have written or to find out more on the topic. Although it is not a skill that will be developed further in this course, you may like to practice it for yourself, when writing your answers.

Question SP12.8 Compare the data in HN Table 12.7 p. 269 with that in HN Table 12.6 p. 268. List the comparisons as a series of four points. Based on this information, what general summary statement could you make about the diet of the young people? ◀

Now complete your study of this chapter by reading the section 'Some potential nutritional problems', HN pp. 273–276.

Question SP12.9 Suppose that you have responsibility for providing nutritional advice to a group of teenagers in your area. List the main aspects of nutrition that you might cover in a leaflet to be distributed to them in school. ◀

Summary of SP12

1   Human milk provides the ideal nutrition for infants, although formula milk is designed to be as close as possible in nutritional content. Human milk has the advantage that it can provide the baby with some protection from infection, due to the presence of antibodies produced by the mother in response to infections that she has encountered, and which the baby might thus be exposed to.

2   Some protein can pass undigested into the bloodstream of infants and weaning too early can induce allergies later. Weaning can safely begin between the ages of about 4 and 6 months.

3   Nutritional requirements are high throughout infancy and energy requirements in relation to body weight are much higher than later in life.

4   A balanced diet is to be encouraged throughout childhood, while allowing the child some choice in what they eat.

5   Influences on diet from outside the home become important during school years and particular nutritional difficulties can arise during teenage years.

Adults and the elderly population

STUDY PERIOD 13

13.1 Adults

This study period considers the diet of adults in the UK.

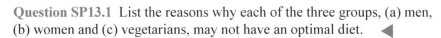

Read the introductory section of HN Chapter 13 and the sections on 'Adult men', 'Adult women' and 'Vegetarians' pp. 279–283.

Question SP13.1 List the reasons why each of the three groups, (a) men, (b) women and (c) vegetarians, may not have an optimal diet. ◀

13.2 Minority ethnic groups

Read the section on 'Minority ethnic groups' from HN pp. 283–288.

Question SP13.2 A family of Orthodox Hindus, recently arrived in the UK from India, have been provided with a leaflet containing the Balance of Good Health plate as shown in Figure SP3.2. Comment on how well their diet in the UK is likely to match each of the food categories on the plate. ◀

13.3 Low income and nutrition

Read HN pp. 288–293, the section on 'Low income and nutrition'.

● Based on the comparisons given in HN Table 13.1 p. 290, which foods are eaten in larger quantities by the highest-income group and which are eaten in larger quantities by the lowest-income group?

● Those in the highest-income group consume more: wholemeal, brown and other bread; breakfast cereal; cheese; fresh green and other vegetables; fruit; fruit juice.

Those in the lowest-income group consume more: white bread; biscuits; milk; meat and meat products; fats and oils; sugars and preserves; potatoes (fresh); processed potatoes and vegetables.

If you have time, you might find it interesting to undertake HN Activity 13.3 p. 293, looking at your own expenditure on food for a week.

Question SP13.3 List the reasons why living on a low income may make it more difficult to eat healthily and to maintain a healthy lifestyle. ◀

13.4 Older adults

Read the section on 'Older adults' HN p. 293 to the end of the chapter, p. 301. HN Figure 13.2 provides a useful summary of the factors that can lead to an inadequate nutritional intake in older adults.

● Why is it important to encourage activity in older adults?

◉ Activity makes people feel more hungry and therefore their total intake of food is likely to increase. This not only provides sufficient energy to balance that used, but also probably provides a wider range of vitamins and minerals than those taken in by inactive people whose intake of food is much less. There is a gradual loss of muscle (lean tissue) in older people. Activity slows down this loss and also helps to maintain cardiovascular fitness and a general feeling of wellbeing.

● HN Table 13.5 p. 299 indicates that the percentage of elderly subjects living in institutions, who have insufficient folate is 5%. HN Table 13.6 p. 300 for the same group of people indicates that 40% of them have insufficient folate. Why is there this difference? You might find it useful to refer back to HN Figure 3.2 p. 42.

◉ The figures in HN Table 13.5 are the percentages of people whose nutrient intakes are below the LRNI, the lower reference nutrient intake. The definition of the LRNI is that it is the amount that would be sufficient for only 2.5% of the population; 97.5% would need more. In elderly subjects living in institutions, 5% have folate intakes below the LRNI. Of these, half do not need more folate (i.e. the 2.5% who need no more than the LNRI), but half (the other 2.5%) need more. 95% of the elderly subjects take in sufficient folate.

The values in HN Table 13.6 are described as 'the prevalence of suboptimal indices', which probably means the percentage of people who have less than the DRV (dietary reference value) (or RNI, reference nutrient intake) for folate. This level would be sufficient for 97.5% of the population. But many people remain healthy on much less than this, as indicated by HN Figure 3.2 p. 42. So the fact that 40% of the elderly people have less than the optimal value is probably not as bad as it looks at first sight.

Question SP13.4 For each of the bulleted statements on p. 300, write an extra sentence or two to explain why this is good advice. For example, the first point is 'Enjoy food', and you might add: 'Many retired people have an energy intake below the EAR. If they ate foods that they enjoyed, they would probably boost their food intake and in doing so also take in a wider range and increased quantities of micronutrients.' ◀

Question SP13.5 Suppose that an elderly relative has recently moved into a care home. Having seen the information in HN Table 13.6, you decide to encourage her to eat more of particular foods to boost her intake of micronutrients. What foods might you advise her to eat? ◀

Summary of SP13

1   The optimum diet of adults should follow the Balance of Good Health guide. There are, however, different needs for men and women and for those on a vegetarian diet.

2   Minority ethnic groups, especially those recently arrived in the UK, have special dietary needs, many related to the integration of their traditional dietary practices with the typical UK diet.

3   Families on low incomes are likely to have a poorer diet than that of higher-income families and attempts have been made to provide advice on eating well on a restricted budget.

4   Older adults can be at risk of inadequate nutrition, largely due to the ageing process itself and the higher prevalence of disease conditions.

5   It is particularly important that elderly people follow the Balance of Good Health guide, have sufficient high-energy foods and sufficient fluids.

Diet and coronary heart disease

This study period is probably the most demanding of Part Three. You will need to work through it slowly and carefully to gain a thorough understanding. It ties together a lot of information from earlier study periods and you will need to go back and re-read sections of those, especially SP5, to refresh your memory and to make the links.

14.1 Introduction to the heart and circulatory system

● What are the names of the three types of blood vessels in the body, and which two types of blood cell have been mentioned?

◐ The blood vessels are arteries, veins and capillaries (SP1.7). The cells are red blood cells which carry the oxygen around the body, and white blood cells whose main function is as part of the immune system, which recognises and destroys 'foreign' cells and molecules that have entered the body.

Arteries are the blood vessels that carry blood away from the heart. They branch many times into smaller, structurally simpler vessels, ending in a huge network of tiny capillaries that run close to every cell in the body, providing it with oxygen. The fact that if you suffer even the tiniest cut on your skin, it begins to bleed, is a good indication that these capillaries are everywhere. Eventually, the tiny capillaries join together again to make larger vessels called veins, that return the blood to the heart (Figure SP14.1).

The main artery taking blood away from the heart to supply oxygenated blood to the body and brain is called the aorta. It is about 25 mm across and the walls are about 2 mm thick. It branches into smaller arteries, called arterioles, about 4 mm in diameter with walls about 1 mm thick and then these continue to branch into yet smaller vessels. The walls of arteries are composed of a special sort of muscle, called smooth muscle, together with collagen and elastin that give strength and springiness to the wall, so that the vessel can widen as a pulse of blood passes through and then spring back to normal (Figure SP14.2). In contrast to arteries, veins have no pulse and are wider, with less muscle and thinner walls. The smaller veins that collect blood from the capillaries are called venules and the large vein that returns the blood to the heart is known as the vena cava. The inside cavity of blood vessels is referred to as the lumen and it is lined by a single layer of cells

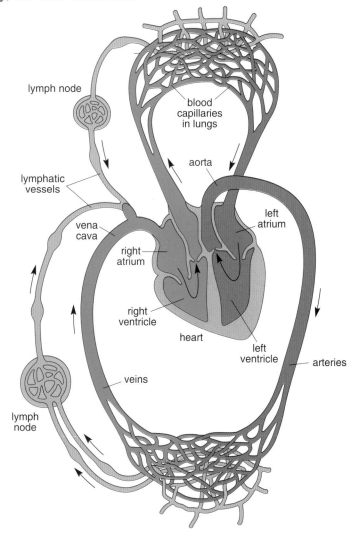

Figure SP14.1 A schematic diagram of the heart, blood and lymph systems, viewed as if facing the body.

called the endothelium. The walls of the tiny capillaries are only composed of a layer of endothelium, which is about one thousandth of a millimetre (1 μm) thick. Capillaries are typically about 5 μm in diameter. Red blood cells can just squeeze through capillaries, often in 'single file'. There are various types of white blood cells such as monocytes and macrophages. Also in the blood are tiny fragments of cells called blood platelets that, together with a chemical in the blood called fibrin, are involved in helping the blood to clot if damage occurs to a blood vessel. The pale-coloured liquid part of the blood is called plasma.

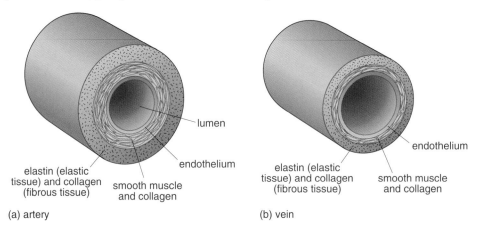

(a) artery (b) vein

Figure SP14.2 Diagrammatic cross-sections of (a) an artery and (b) a vein.

Figure SP 14.1 also shows the lymph system, which is composed of lymphatics (lymphatic vessels) and lymph nodes.

● Look back to Figure SP5.9. What function of the lymphatics did you meet there?

◐ Lymphatics are the vessels into which the chylomicrons, produced at the end of the process of fat digestion, are absorbed, on their way to the bloodstream.

Excess fluid from the tissues is also absorbed into the lymphatics. Movement of the body's muscles pushes the lymph fluid along the lymphatics until it is returned to the blood system near the heart. The larger lymphatics are similar in structure to veins. Lymph nodes are involved in the production of white blood cells called lymphocytes, which are an important part of the immune system.

The heart is a pump with four chambers, two atria (singular, atrium), which collect the blood as it enters the heart, and two ventricles, which pump the blood out again. The blood vessels entering and leaving the heart form two separate circuits. The first is from the heart to the lungs and back to the heart. During this circuit, the blood picks up oxygen from the air in the lungs. This oxygenated blood, which is a bright red, is then pumped around the second circuit which supplies blood to all parts of the body. The oxygen from the blood is used by the cells, and so blood returning to the heart contains less oxygen (deoxygenated blood) and is a much duller red (shown as blue on Figure SP14.1). The heart then pumps it around the first circuit again back to the lungs to pick up more oxygen. Of course, some blood is pumped around both circuits with each heartbeat, with the heart beating roughly once a second when a person is resting. When the heart muscle is contracting, the pressure in the arteries is greatest. This is known as the systolic blood pressure, which is typically in the range 100 to 140 mmHg. The pressure in the arteries when the heart is relaxing between beats is the diastolic blood pressure, with a normal value of between 50 and 90 mmHg.

● Can you work out what the units 'mmHg' might mean?

◔ You probably realised that mm represents millimetres. Hg is the chemical symbol for the element mercury, so mmHg is read as 'millimetres of mercury'.

The unit derives from the now outdated instrument used to measure blood pressure, called a sphygmomanometer, which has a glass column containing mercury and an inflatable rubber cuff that is placed around the upper arm at the level of the heart. The units refer to the height of the mercury in the tube, which is a measure of the pressure in the cuff. The cuff is inflated until no sound of the heartbeat is heard, using a stethoscope on the artery in the elbow. The cuff is then deflated until the sound of the heartbeat just reappears. The pressure in the cuff is then equal to the systolic pressure. As the cuff is allowed to deflate further, the sound of the heartbeat is heard until the cuff is no longer restricting the blood flow at all. At this point the sound becomes muffled as the blood runs smoothly again and this is a measure of the diastolic pressure. Current (2005) medical advice is that if the systolic reading is higher than 140 mmHg, or the diastolic reading higher than 90 mmHg, the measurement is high and the person may be suffering from high blood pressure or hypertension. However, due to a common reaction known as 'white coat hypertension', i.e. a rise in blood pressure due to the stress of seeing a doctor, no reliance should be placed on a single high reading.

Since the heart itself is composed largely of muscle, it needs its own supply of oxygenated blood, to enable it to contract efficiently. This supply comes from blood vessels called coronary arteries (shown in the diagram of the surface view of the heart in HN Figure 14.1 p. 306). As you will see later, there are several ways in which these arteries can become either partially or totally blocked. Such blockages constitute coronary heart disease (CHD). Partial blockage results in bouts of chest pain called angina, which can be relieved by drugs and, if severe, by heart bypass surgery: the surgeon takes a length of blood vessel from elsewhere in the body and grafts it in place to provide a new route for the blood to bypass the blockage. A heart attack (or myocardial infarction) is a complete blockage that happens suddenly, stopping the heart beat. If, on the other hand, a blood vessel in the brain becomes blocked, then cells in the part of the brain supplied by that vessel are deprived of oxygen and may die, so that some brain function is lost. This condition is called a stroke (or cerebrovascular accident).

Question SP14.1 (a) Describe in words the structure of the wall of an artery, as illustrated in Figure SP14.2a.

(b) How does the wall of a vein differ from that of an artery? ◀

The heart and all the blood vessels are referred to as the cardiovascular system and any failure of this system to function as it should, or damage to the system, is termed cardiovascular disease. Coronary heart disease (CHD) and strokes are the main two types of cardiovascular disease and are major causes of death in the UK. The study of the causes of diseases such as CHD is called aetiology. Death rates due to cardiovascular disease vary between countries and in part depend on the age structure in the population. In a developing country where death rates amongst children and young adults are high, there are relatively few elderly people. Since cardiovascular disease generally affects older people, the death rate from this cause may be quite low. In countries like the UK where both the infant mortality rate and the mortality rate of younger adults are low, there are relatively larger numbers of elderly people and so a relatively higher mortality rate from cardiovascular disease. So, to allow better comparison between these different populations, the mortality figures are adjusted to take account of the age structure of the population. These are referred to as 'age standardised' mortality rates.

14.2 The biology of a heart attack

● What is LDL?

◉ The letters LDL stand for low density lipoprotein. LDL consists of fat, mostly cholesterol, and protein. High levels of LDL in the blood (compared with HDL or high density lipoproteins) are linked with an increased risk of coronary heart disease. (SP5.4.3)

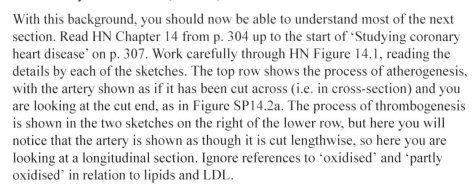

With this background, you should now be able to understand most of the next section. Read HN Chapter 14 from p. 304 up to the start of 'Studying coronary heart disease' on p. 307. Work carefully through HN Figure 14.1, reading the details by each of the sketches. The top row shows the process of atherogenesis, with the artery shown as if it has been cut across (i.e. in cross-section) and you are looking at the cut end, as in Figure SP14.2a. The process of thrombogenesis is shown in the two sketches on the right of the lower row, but here you will notice that the artery is shown as though it is cut lengthwise, so here you are looking at a longitudinal section. Ignore references to 'oxidised' and 'partly oxidised' in relation to lipids and LDL.

Question SP14.2 Based mainly on HN Figure 14.1, describe, in your own words, the process of (a) atherogenesis and (b) thrombogenesis. ◀

14.3 Studying coronary heart disease

There are important links, as you will soon read, between the incidence of CHD and blood cholesterol levels. So it would be useful here to revise what you have already read about cholesterol (SP5.4.2) and to learn a little more.

Question SP14.3 Shown here is the structural formula of cholesterol as it would be drawn by a chemist. You will immediately notice that the symbols of only two atoms are given.

(a) In this abbreviated form, all of the carbon atoms and the hydrogen atoms attached to them have been omitted (as in Figure SP9.1). Sketch out the cholesterol molecule showing all of its carbon and hydrogen atoms, but grouping them together as, for example CH_2. Remember that there is a carbon atom at each of the 'corners' and at the end of each of the 'sticks', that all carbon atoms must have the correct number of bonds, and that any spare bonds must be occupied by hydrogen.

(b) Check back to the description of the cholesterol molecule in SP5.4.2 and confirm that your drawing of the molecule fits this description.

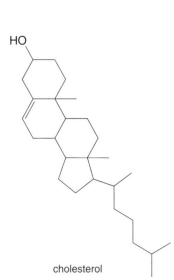

HO

cholesterol

(c) Why is cholesterol classed as a lipid despite its rather different structure from triacylglycerols?

(d) What are the important roles of cholesterol in the body? ◀

Read the section 'Studying coronary heart disease', HN pp. 307–309, and then check your understanding by answering this series of short questions.

● What is meant by 'the absence of a close animal model for myocardial infarction'?

◍ It means that scientists have not found a strain of rats or mice or other convenient laboratory animal that suffers heart attacks due to the blockage of a coronary artery in a similar way to humans.

● In the Keys' Seven Country Study, which aspect of diet was found to have the strongest link with the incidence of CHD?

◍ The strongest link with CHD was with the percentage of energy in the diet that is derived from saturated fat. (The dietary recommendation is that only about 11% of the total energy needs of the body should be met by saturated fat – see HN Table 12.6, p. 268.)

● Look back to your completed Table SP5.1 to identify which foods should be reduced in the diet in order to limit the intake of saturated fat.

◍ Saturated fats (those with no double bonds) are found mostly in animal fats such as butter, beef fat, lard and synthetic fats such as hard margarine. So reducing the dietary intake of these and replacing them where possible with oils should be beneficial.

● What is meant by the sentence 'The strongest correlation was found between the percentage of energy derived from saturated fat in the diet and increased risk of heart disease' (HN p. 307)?

◍ It means that those people in whom a high percentage of their energy is derived from the saturated fat in their diet, have a greater risk of developing heart disease than those whose diet is such that a lower percentage of their energy is derived from saturated fat.

You will recall that the opposite of this, where one factor goes up and the other goes down, is called a negative correlation, or a reciprocal relationship. This type of relationship occurs between the intake of polyunsaturated fats and heart disease, though this relationship is described as 'weaker' indicating that there is a variable and only slight decline in heart disease as polyunsaturated fats in the diet increase.

● What is meant by 'serum' in the phrase 'serum cholesterol'?

◍ Serum is the liquid part of blood; the word has a similar meaning to blood 'plasma'. However, serum is the liquid obtained when the blood has been allowed to clot, so it does not include some of the factors in the blood that are involved in the clotting process. Blood plasma, on the other hand, is obtained by allowing the cells to settle out (or by spinning the blood in a centrifuge to speed up the process) without allowing it to clot. In relation to levels of cholesterol in the blood, the words are often used interchangeably.

● What does the Keys formula show?

◉ It expresses a link between the intake of saturated and polyunsaturated fatty acids (derived from the digestion of the mixture of fats in the diet) on cholesterol levels in the blood. A higher intake of saturated fatty acids is associated with higher blood cholesterol levels, while more polyunsaturated fatty acids in the diet is linked to lower blood cholesterol. But the effect of the saturated fatty acids is twice as great as the effect of the polyunsaturated fatty acids. So the ratio of polyunsaturated fatty acids to saturated fatty acids in the diet should be as high as possible, ideally around 0.5–0.8.

● What is a prospective study?

◉ A prospective study starts with a large number of individuals and follows them through life, collecting data about their diet, health, etc., from them at intervals.

● What did data from the Framingham study show to be the main contributory risk factors in CHD?

◉ This study showed that people with raised blood cholesterol levels, high blood pressure and who smoked cigarettes were more at risk of developing CHD.

● What dietary improvements were made in those living in North Karelia, Finland that appeared to result in large reductions in CHD in both men and women?

◉ They changed from butter to margarines made from vegetable oil, they changed from whole milk to low-fat milk and from boiled to filtered coffee. They also reduced their salt intake and increased the amount of fruit and vegetables in their diet.

● What concerns have been raised as a result of trials involving cholesterol-lowering drugs?

◉ Some studies have shown that giving cholesterol-lowering drugs to people who do not have CHD does reduce the mortality from CHD but increases the deaths due to other causes. So lowering blood cholesterol in this way may not be the ideal solution.

● One study showed that addition of long-chain n-3 fatty acids to the diet resulted in a 20% reduction in mortality from CHD. Look back to Table SP5.1 and identify what foods a person might eat to add these particular fatty acids.

◉ Oily fish is the richest source, but also leafy vegetables, poultry meat, and certain nuts could be consumed.

● Look carefully at the graph in HN Figure 14.2. Describe the measurements shown on each of the axes. Then describe each of the curves.

◉ The vertical (y) axis of the graph gives the (age-adjusted) death rate per 1000 men over a period of six years and runs from 0 to 40. The horizontal (x) axis shows the blood (plasma) cholesterol level, measured in two different units. The upper of the scales gives the concentration of cholesterol in the plasma, measured in milligrams of cholesterol per decilitre of blood (mg/dl) where one decilitre is a tenth of a litre, i.e. 100 ml. (You probably know that the concentration of alcohol in blood is usually expressed in the same units, i.e. mg per 100 ml blood.) The concentration of any substance can alternatively be expressed in units called mmol/L, millimoles per litre (as you met for blood glucose levels in SP6.2.1). This unit of measurement takes into account the size of the molecule, cholesterol in this case, and you will notice that the two values for cholesterol are a factor of 40 different; so it is easy to convert from one to the other by multiplying or dividing by 40, as appropriate.

The upper curve indicates that the total mortality (that is, death from all causes) in a group of 1000 men during a period of 6 years ranges from about 15 to about 40. The lowest death rate does not correspond to the lowest cholesterol level. The death rate appears to be around 25 per 1000 in men with blood cholesterol levels around 140 mg/dl and then falls to around 20 deaths for cholesterol levels around 200 mg/dl. It then rises to about 40 deaths per 1000 men for cholesterol levels around 320 mg/dl.

Meanwhile, deaths from coronary heart disease (CHD) do seem to be directly related to the blood cholesterol level and rise from less than 5 per 1000 at a cholesterol level of around 140 mg/dl to around 20 at 320 mg/dl.

You may have noticed an inconsistency in the units in HN Figure 14.2. Litres can be abbreviated as L or l. Here decilitre is given as dl, whereas litre is given as L.

Question SP14.4 The Keys formula expresses the ratio of polyunsaturated to saturated fats in the diet (P/S) and recommends that the desirable goal is a ratio of 0.5–0.8.

(a) What fraction of the dietary intake of fats should be polyunsaturated to produce a P/S ratio of 0.5?

(b) What fraction of the dietary intake of fats should be polyunsaturated to produce a P/S ratio of 0.8?

(c) What general dietary advice would you give to someone who wanted to increase their P/S ratio and therefore reduce their risk of CHD? ◀

14.4 Risk factors

Read HN from p. 309 until towards the end of p. 313, the beginning of the 'Dietary factors' section.

● Look carefully at HN Figure 14.3 p. 310 and identify two aspects of the vertical axis of this graph which are puzzling, and one other aspect of the graph where the meaning is not clear.

◉ The vertical axis of the graph is labelled 'Coronary surface covered (%)'. It is not clear from the figure what is meant by 'coronary surface covered'. Does it mean the surface of the heart is covered with fatty deposits? The caption refers to 'damage to coronary arteries' and it is not at all clear how this relates to 'coronary surface covered'. Secondly, the axis runs from 0 to 120%. Since 100% would be wholly covered, it is not possible to have values higher than this.

The other aspect of the graph whose meaning is not clear is the labelling of the lines of the graph. The lowest line is labelled 'Plasma cholesterol level of 5.2 mmol/L' and then the steeper lines are labelled '+ Smoking', '+ Hypertension' and '+ Diabetes'. It is not clear whether each line represents the additional effect of that single risk factor or whether the risk factors are cumulative, i.e. the line labelled '+ Diabetes' means the additional effect of diabetes on someone who already has hypertension and who smokes.

The only way to resolve these issues is to go back to the original scientific paper from which the graph has been taken. The caption gives the author's name as Grundy and the date of the paper as 1988, and the list of references, at the end of HN Chapter 14 (p. 322), provides the remaining details. Unfortunately, the date has been mistyped and the paper was published in 1986. However, having tracked it down in the Journal of the American Medical Association, the figure in the paper, reproduced here as Figure SP14.3, provides answers to the puzzles.

● Look carefully at Figure SP14.3. How does it address the issues raised in the question above?

◑ The meaning of '% coronary surface covered' is made clearer by the caption which refers to the 'percentage of surface of coronary arteries covered with raised lesions'. The 'surface' here refers to the internal surface of the coronary arteries and the word 'lesion' refers to the fibrous plaques, shown in HN Figure 14.1 p. 306, that cause narrowing of the vessels. The problem with the axis being labelled with values over 100% is resolved too. This was obviously an error in the copying of the figure, since the original axis is labelled only up to 90% and the lines terminate at about the position where 100% would be. The figure caption also clarifies the third issue, indicating that the risk factors are cumulative, i.e. the steepest line represents the effect of smoking, hypertension and diabetes together. You may also have noticed that the value of the plasma cholesterol level given in the original paper was 5.17 mmol/L, which has been rounded to 5.2 mmol/L in HN Figure 14.3. 'Critical stenosis' is the situation where the coronary arteries are narrowed to such an extent that a heart attack is imminent, which occurs when 60% of the internal surface of the coronary arteries is covered with plaques and is represented by the horizontal dashed line on the graph. The graph shows that this level of blockage is reached when someone with a cholesterol level of 5.17 mmol/L reaches the age of 70. If this person smokes, then they will typically reach it at the age of about 60. If they have high blood pressure too, then they are at risk of a heart attack at about 50, and if additionally they suffer from diabetes then a heart attack is likely at 40 years of age.

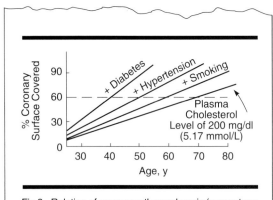

Fig 8.–Relation of coronary atherosclerosis (percentage of surface of coronary arteries covered with raised lesions) vs age as modified by addition of risk factors. In absence of other risk factors, patient with cholesterol level of 200 mg/dl (5.17 mmol/L) should reach critical stenosis at about age 70 years. Addition of smoking reduces age to 60 years, and addition of more risk factors (i.e. hypertension and diabetes mellitus) reduces age further.

Figure SP14.3 Figure reproduced from Grundy, S.M., 1986, *Journal of the American Medical Association*, vol. **256**, p. 2856.

Question SP14.5 Based on the description of HN Figure 14.3 just given, write your own description of HN Figure 14.5 on p. 311. ◀

Question SP14.6 For each of the 12 risk factors in the section you have just read, write a single sentence describing how they affect the risk of developing CHD. ◀

14.5 Dietary factors

Before you tackle the final part of HN Chapter 14, you should re-read SP5.3.6 Melting temperatures and SP5.4.3 Lipoproteins.

● What are *trans* fatty acids and where do they occur?

◐ *Trans* fatty acids are unsaturated fatty acids that have the atoms on either side of the double bond(s) arranged in a particular way, such that the double bond produces only a small bend in the molecule (*cis* fatty acids have a large bend). They are produced in the manufacture of hard margarine and occur naturally in meat, milk, butter, etc. from ruminant animals like cows and sheep.

● Explain what is meant by LDL cholesterol and HDL cholesterol. Which one increases the risk of CHD?

◐ A small fraction of the total body complement of cholesterol is carried around the body attached to lipoproteins in the blood. Low density lipoproteins (LDL) carry less cholesterol than high density lipoproteins (HDL). HDL is recognised as 'good' cholesterol. LDL is the form that is linked with the formation of fibrous plaques inside arteries (atherogenesis) (see HN Figure 14.1) and increases the risk of heart attacks.

When scientists have to remember rather similar terms, they often make up a 'mnemonic' (the first 'm' is silent), as an aide-mémoire. Since HDL is the 'good' form, you might remember the H as also standing for 'happy'. LDL is the dangerous form, so you might think of the L as also standing for 'lousy' or 'loathsome'. Of course, it doesn't matter what mnemonic you choose as long as **you** can remember it!

The last part of this chapter covering 'Dietary factors' (pp. 313–321) contains more detail than you need for the purposes of this course. You should try to grasp the main points of each section, without getting too bogged down in all the details. If you come across a word that you have not met before, then you can just ignore it. We have introduced you to all those that you need for the purposes of this course. You do not need to study the sections 'Mechanisms of action of antioxidants', 'Endogenous antioxidants' and 'Exogenous antioxidants' (pp. 319–320). You will find it useful to have your completed Table SP5.1 'Names and properties of a selection of fatty acids' beside you as your read this section. HN Figure 14.6 provides a useful summary of the possible dietary factors that increase the risk of suffering from CHD and those that are protective. You should spend some time working carefully through that figure, as you read HN pp. 313–318.

Summary of SP14

1 Cardiovascular disease, which includes coronary heart disease (CHD) and strokes, accounts for about 40% of deaths in the UK.

2 Atherogenesis (the formation of fibrous plaques in coronary arteries) and thrombogenesis (the formation of clots around fragments of such plaques) lead to myocardial infarctions (heart attacks).

3 Large numbers of risk factors, many unrelated to diet, for coronary heart disease (CHD) have been identified.

4 Amongst the dietary factors, the composition and total amount of fats taken in are important, together with levels of salt, calcium, alcohol, fibre, antioxidants and homocysteine.

Diet and cancer

15.1 Cell division and cancer

In SP1, you were introduced to 'cells' as the tiny subunits that make up humans, and all living things. In humans, these cells are all derived from a fertilised egg, that has a set of 46 chromosomes in its nucleus, 23 from each parent. Each time the cell divides into two, the chromosomes are copied, so that each new cell also has 46 chromosomes.

● How many cell divisions occur to form a ball of eight cells?

◉ The first division produces two cells. Division of each of those makes a total of four cells and one more division of each of those gives a total of eight cells. So three rounds of division forms a ball of eight cells.

At the earliest stages, the cells all look much the same, but soon different types of cell begin to appear and before long there are numerous different types of cell and the ball of cells begins to look like a fetus. By about eight weeks after conception, the fetus is recognisably human. It then continues to grow and develop until birth, although no new cell types are made. Growth then continues until adulthood. Throughout growth, new cells are needed, so some cells retain the ability to divide. Others have changed (differentiated) so that they can perform a specific function, such as becoming nerve cells or red blood cells or bone cells. During differentiation, some cell types lose the ability to divide.

● Why do some cell types need to continue to divide in adults, when growth is complete?

◉ New cells are needed to replace those that are damaged or die or are lost from the body. Perhaps the scar tissue formed when a wound heals is the most obvious example of where new cells are required. Cells are also shed continuously from the surface of the skin and from the lining of the gut and must be replaced by newly produced ones. Cells in the bone marrow divide and mature to become red blood cells at a rate of about one and a half million per second.

A special type of cell division occurs to generate the reproductive cells, eggs and sperm, together known as gametes. The remainder of the cells in the body are collectively known as somatic cells.

● How many chromosomes are present in each gamete?

◉ Since there are 46 chromosomes in a fertilised egg, 23 from each parent, then there must be 23 chromosomes in each gamete.

It is not surprising that the process of cell division must be carefully controlled so that sufficient cells of the various types are produced as required – but not too many. Occasionally, an abnormality develops in an individual cell and this control mechanism fails. The cell may begin to divide uncontrollably and this is the start of cancer.

● From HN Table 15.1 p. 326, identify those factors that can initiate the development of cancer.

● The factors are:

- Harmful chemicals, called carcinogens (cancer-causing)
- Certain viruses
- Free radicals
- Some forms of radiation (UV rays, high doses of X-rays, emissions from radioactive atoms, etc.)
- Errors that occur when the information in the DNA in the chromosomes is used to make proteins
- A genetic predisposition to cancer; some cancers run in families.

More than one of these factors usually needs to be present for cancer to develop and there are other factors, as indicated in HN Table 15.1, that can inhibit the development of cancer even after the first step has occurred.

Now read HN Chapter 15 pp. 324–327, up to the start of the 'Environmental causes of cancer' section.

● Imagine that in a particular population whose diet contained a high proportion of shellfish, you found unexpectedly large numbers of people with a rare form of throat cancer. Would you be right to conclude that the shellfish diet was the cause of the throat cancer?

● No, you would not. A positive correlation of this sort – more shellfish, more throat cancer – does not prove causality. Something entirely different, such as another component in the diet or some contamination in the drinking water or some completely unknown factor, could be the cause of the cancer. Further research would be needed to identify a specific mechanism that could support the link, alongside experimental studies if possible, such as removing the shellfish from the diet and seeing if cancers still occurred.

15.2 Environmental causes of cancer

Read HN pp. 327–334, concentrating on the factors in the diet that are thought to promote the development of cancer and those factors that are thought to be protective. You need not worry about the chemistry of the compounds that you have not already met, nor details of how the various factors exert their effects. In fact, as you will read, many of the links are not yet understood. You might find it useful to list all the possible promoting and protective factors, with a short summary, as you did in Question SP14.6. You could compare your list with HN Figure 15.1 which provides a useful summary.

15.3 Prevention of cancer

Read the remainder of HN Chapter 15 pp. 334–336. HN Table 15.3 is a summary of the public health advice and the advice to individuals from the World Cancer Research Fund (WCRF) report in 1997. It refers to PAL, which stands for physical activity level (a term you met in SP7.4.2):

$$\text{physical activity level, PAL} = \frac{\text{total energy expenditure}}{\text{resting energy expenditure}}$$

If a person has 8 hours of sleep and spends the remaining 16 hours doing nothing more than washing, dressing and sitting or standing around, their PAL is about 1.27. An office worker probably has a PAL of about 1.4. Thirty minutes brisk walking a day raises this person's PAL to about 1.55. Significantly more exercise is needed to raise the PAL to the value of 1.75 suggested by the WCRF.

Question SP15.1 How does the dietary advice to individuals in the WCRF report compare with the UK Balance of Good Health (BGH) guidelines as shown in Figure SP3.2? Deal with each relevant statement in the WCRF report in turn. ◀

Figure SP15.1 items:
1 medium apple
2 broccoli florets
2 halves of canned peaches
1 handful of grapes
1 medium banana
3 heaped tablespoons of peas
1 medium glass of orange juice
7 strawberries
3 whole dried apricots
5 A DAY
Just Eat More (fruit & veg)
www.doh.gov.uk/fiveaday
3 heaped tablespoons of cooked kidney beans
16 okra
NHS

Figure SP15.1 Cover of a leaflet produced by the UK Department of Health in 2003.

Activity SP15.1

The different ways in which dietary advice is provided by different organisations for different audiences shows some interesting contrasts, as you have seen in Question SP15.1. Look through the articles and leaflets that you have been collecting to see if you have any that give dietary advice. Consider the audience at which any such information is targeted and compare it with the WCRF guidelines and the BGH plate. For example, the cover of a leaflet produced by the UK Department of Health shows very clearly what constitutes a 'portion' as part of the campaign to encourage people to eat five portions of fruit and vegetables each day (Figure SP15.1).

Summary of SP15

1 Cell division is normally well controlled. When cells begin to divide in an uncontrolled manner, cancer develops.

2 There is no single cause of cancer; several factors can be involved.

3 Diet is an important factor in relation to cancer; some substances in the diet have been identified as promoters of cancer, others have a protective effect.

4 In particular, high total energy in the diet, high fat intakes, high intakes of alcohol, salt and processed meat are possible cancer-promoting factors.

5 Protecting factors are increased exercise and diets containing significant NSP, fruit and vegetables, milk and dairy products and n-3 fatty acids.

6 The recommended diet containing protecting factors against cancer is similar to the eight guidelines for a healthy diet and the Balance of Good Health plate, though differences do exist.

Challenges to nutritional status

16.1 Introduction

This study period covers several situations in which there is an additional threat to a person's nutritional status. Here you will discover how the food intake and its subsequent use in the body can be affected by: infections, especially HIV; particularly high use of energy, as in athletes; alcohol abuse; and disability. However, the first topic is adverse reactions to food, and to understand some of these, some background information on the human immune system is necessary.

16.2 The immune system

The immune system protects the body from substances that are potentially harmful, mostly infectious organisms and parasites, by reacting to any substances in the body that are recognised as foreign (non-self) (SP12.2). This is called the immune response.

● Antibodies are one component of the immune system. What are antibodies?

◉ Antibodies are proteins produced by white blood cells. They help to destroy foreign (non-self) substances that get into the body.

Antibodies are also called immunoglobulins; 'immuno' means that they are part of the immune system and 'globulin' refers to a globular type of protein (SP4.6.3). There are five types of immunoglobulin, of which two are important here; immunoglobulin A, referred to as IgA, and immunoglobulin E, IgE. The foreign substances that stimulate the production of antibodies are called antigens. Except in babies up to a few months old, a protective coat of IgA antibodies lines the digestive system. They bind to the many substances in food that are potential antigens, and so prevent any further immune response to them. However, in some people, an inappropriate allergic response does occur to certain food molecules. Substances that provoke such a response are known as allergens and the person is said to have a food allergy.

A particular type of cell, called a mast cell, is an essential component of the immune response. Mast cells are found in various sites in the body where foreign molecules are likely to be encountered, such as the lower layer of the skin, called the dermis, and the wall of the digestive system, called the submucosa. When the body is challenged by an antigen, IgE antibodies attach to the mast cells and trigger them to release a range of chemicals, including histamine and prostaglandins, that initiate the allergic response. HN p. 341 gives lists of responses and places where they may occur, and the allergic response to food is illustrated in HN Figure 16.2. You might find it useful to look at these now.

16.3 Adverse reactions to food

Read HN Chapter 16 from p. 338 to the start of the section on 'Nutrition in HIV infection and AIDS' on p. 347.

● At the start of p. 342 is a mention of the necessity for an adrenalin injection for someone suffering a major allergic response. Why do most people not need such an injection?

◉ Normally, the body keeps its own internal environment constant by feedback mechanisms that counteract any disruption. This process is called homeostasis (see SP10.2.1). One of the homeostatic responses to an allergen is the production by the body of its own adrenalin (called 'endogenous adrenalin release').

● What two reasons have been proposed to explain the increase in food and other allergies over the past 30 years?

◉ Since children now live in cleaner environments and are exposed to fewer infectious diseases, their immune system may be less 'challenged' at an early age and may therefore respond inappropriately later.

Modern diets contain fewer *n*-3 fatty acids and more *n*-6 fatty acids than in times past. Both are the raw material for the synthesis of prostaglandins and other lipid-based messenger molecules that play important roles in allergic responses.

● What do you understand by 'pharmacologically active agents' (towards the end of p. 343)?

◉ Pharmacology is the study of drugs, so pharmacologically active agents would be those that behave like drugs in the body.

● Why do prunes act as a mild laxative?

◉ Prunes contain a compound called hydroxyphenylisatin, which stimulates movement of the gut ('intestinal motor activity') and therefore results in the faster movement of food along the digestive tract.

● Since food colours and other additives are reported to cause adverse reactions in some people, why is it still acceptable for them to be used?

◉ Many additives act as preservatives, preventing the food deteriorating or being contaminated with harmful bacteria. Since more people are potentially at risk from infection than suffer adverse reactions to the additives, overall it is beneficial for them to be added. Food colours, however, are generally included simply to make the food more appealing to the eye, so they may benefit the food manufacturer, since consumers are likely to buy more of their product, rather more than they benefit the consumer. However, if the colouring does make a food with an important nutritional role more appealing to children, for example, then that might provide some justification for its continued use.

● What is lactase and why does it disappear from the body after infancy? You may need to refer back to SP6.6.

◐ Lactase is an enzyme that breaks up the disaccharide lactose, the main sugar present in milk. Remember that names of sugar molecules usually end in -ose, while the enzymes that digest them end in -ase. Since milk is an essential form of nutrition for babies, it is important that the enzyme lactase is present. Older children and adults are much less dependent on milk for their nutrition and lactase is therefore no longer essential. In fact, before animals were domesticated, and in many areas today, milk is absent from the post-weaning diet.

● What is meant by a 'double blind technique' and why might it be used?

◐ It is an experiment, for example to identify food allergies in a person, in which neither the person conducting the experiment, nor the person who is being tested, know when the food being tested is introduced. It is used to avoid any bias that might be introduced by either side if they knew which food was which.

● List those aspects of the diet that are thought to improve the functioning of the immune system.

◐ Sufficient protein; a reduction in total fat but eating foods containing plenty of unsaturated fatty acids; appropriate intake of vitamins and minerals, especially vitamins A, B_6, B_{12}, folic acid and vitamins C and E, zinc, iron (although excess iron depresses immune function too) and selenium.

16.4 Nutrition, AIDS and drugs

Read HN pp. 347–351, stopping before 'Nutrition and the athlete'. You are not expected to understand any of the details in the 'Drug–nutrient interactions' section and if you are short of time, you could omit this section. Note that enteral feeding means providing nutrition directly into the stomach or intestines, in liquid form, through a tube. In parenteral nutrition, the nutrients are delivered directly into the bloodstream.

Question SP16.1 Write a sentence or two on each of the factors that appear to be linked with weight loss in patients with HIV infection. ◀

16.5 Nutrition and the athlete

● What is the name of the molecule that the body uses as its very short-term energy store? Check back in SP8.3.3.

◐ It is ATP, adenosine triphosphate.

ATP is the molecule that provides energy in a form that enables muscles to contract. It is possible to purchase ATP in a bottle from chemical suppliers. When made into a solution and dropped onto a few fibres taken from a piece of very fresh raw steak, it provides them with the energy to contract by a measurable amount. However, ATP is very soon used up. HN Figure 16.5 shows that there is enough ATP in muscles to last for about three seconds, by which time it has all been exhausted. ATP contains three phosphate groups (hence triphosphate in the name). The process of 'using up' ATP breaks it down into ADP (adenosine diphosphate) and a free phosphate ion. To regenerate the ATP, either there has to be a source of energy for these breakdown products to be reattached, or a phosphate group has to be supplied by another molecule. The molecule creatine phosphate, also found in muscle, is a source of such phosphate groups and there is sufficient of it in the body to last about 15 seconds. After that, ATP can only be regenerated by breaking down fats or carbohydrate, usually glucose, in the muscles, using oxygen. If exercise is vigorous, insufficient oxygen is likely to be available for this process. Glucose is then broken down in a process that does not need oxygen to produce some energy to regenerate ATP. However, this anaerobic process produces lactic acid, that rapidly builds up in the muscles, and before long the muscles no longer contract and the exercise has to stop. It is the lactic acid that makes your muscles ache when you exercise. Some deep breaths supply more oxygen to the muscles and allow the lactic acid to be removed from the tissues, and broken down in the liver, so that exercise can resume.

Read the section on 'Nutrition and the athlete' from HN pp. 351–357.

Question SP16.2 In about 250 words, describe the bar chart HN Figure 16.6. What conclusion can be drawn from the information given there? ◀

Question SP16.3 An athlete might need an intake of 21 MJ each day (1 MJ = 1000 kJ) and about 60% of this energy should come from carbohydrates.

(a) How many grams of carbohydrate would need to be consumed each day? You will need data from Table SP7.1.

(b) Potatoes contain about 17% carbohydrate (Table SP6.2). How many grams would need to be eaten to provide the requisite amount of carbohydrate?

(c) Baked beans in tomato sauce contain about 10 g of carbohydrate per 100 g. How many grams of baked beans would be needed to provide the requisite amount of carbohydrate? ◀

Question SP16.4 HN Table 16.1 lists foods according to their glycaemic index (GI), that you first met in SP6.8 in relation to weight control. Explain why a person wishing to lose weight should consume foods with a low glycaemic index whereas after exercise, athletes should consume foods with a high glycaemic index. ◀

16.6 Effects of alcohol abuse and disability on nutrition

Now complete SP16 by reading HN p. 357 to the end of the chapter on p. 362.

Question SP16.5 At the start of HN Chapter 16, the author describes 'intake – processing – utilization' as a useful framework for considering challenges to nutritional status. Describe, in a few sentences for each, which parts of this pathway are affected in a person who has (a) excess alcohol intake and (b) a disability that affects their muscle control. ◀

Summary of SP16

1   Food allergies can be linked to the abnormal functioning of the immune system.

2   Weight loss is a major problem in patients with HIV/AIDS and correct nutrition is therefore a particularly important factor.

3   Athletes have particular nutritional requirements due to their increased use of energy. High GI foods are recommended after exercise.

4   Excessive intake of alcohol is a major threat to all stages of the nutrient 'intake–processing–utilisation' sequence.

5   Many forms of disability are likely to affect nutrition.

STUDY PERIOD # 17

Optimising nutrition

17.1 Introduction

The concept of optimal nutrition is a relatively recent one and moves on from food supplying the nutrients that the body requires, to consideration of whether there are health benefits from certain components of food. These components may or may not also have conventional nutritional roles. In this study period, you will find out about some of these components. You should be able to work though HN Chapter 17 more quickly than many of the previous ones. The names of many chemicals are given, but you are not expected to understand or remember them. It is more important that you get a general overview of this developing area of nutrition.

17.2 Foods and health

Read through the whole of HN Chapter 17, pp. 364–378.

Question SP17.1 Write about 200 words describing the differences between a food that is said to have a specific effect on health and a drug (medicine). ◀

Question SP17.2 Olestra (HN p. 367) is a fat substitute, that has almost no nutritional value, but nevertheless smells and tastes like fat. It is composed of fatty acids attached to a sucrose molecule.

(a) In a normal fat molecule, what substance are the fatty acids attached to and which atoms, or groups of atoms, are involved in making the bond? You may need to look back to SP5.3.3.

(b) Based on your answer to (a), and using Figure SP17.1, how many fatty acids would theoretically be able to link to a sucrose molecule?

(c) What features of the Olestra molecule prevent it from being absorbed from the digestive tract? SP5.5 will help. ◀

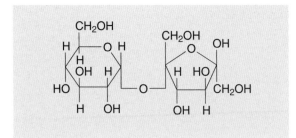

Figure SP17.1 The structural formula of sucrose.

Question SP17.3 Explain, with examples, the difference between the following pairs of terms:

(a) functional foods and fortified foods;

(b) vitamins and phytochemicals;

(c) probiotics and prebiotics. ◀

Question SP17.4 What advice might you give to a friend on whether or not they should buy more costly organic vegetables for their family? ◀

Activity SP17.1

(a) Identify two foods, either in your own diet or by looking at food labels on supermarket shelves, that are fortified with extra vitamins, and list the vitamins added.

(b) Choose two of the added vitamins. Do either of the foods you chose make a major contribution to your daily intake of those vitamins? What other sources of the vitamins exist in your diet? You will need to refer back to Table SP9.1.

In addition to optimising nutrition for the general population, there is now considerable work in progress on optimising nutrition for individuals, based on their genetic profile (the combination of genes that they carry). For example, if genetic testing showed that an individual had a gene or combination of genes that put them at greater risk of CHD than normal, they could be encouraged to consume a particular diet from an early age. Ultimately, it might be possible to check the genetic profile of every newborn baby and plan appropriate diets for that individual at all stages of their life, detailing which foods they should avoid and what quantities of others they should be consuming. As well as raising considerable ethical issues, this could make eating much less fun! There are likely to be significant developments in this area of nutrition in the next few years.

Summary of SP17

1   Optimal nutrition recognises that certain components of foods, which may or may not have a nutritional role, are beneficial to health.

2   Functional foods have been produced that have health-promoting benefits, such as those fortified with vitamins, sports drinks for athletes and probiotics to improve the balance of gut microbes.

3   Organic food is not necessarily better for human health than conventionally produced food.

Answer to Activity SP17.1

(a) You may have chosen a breakfast cereal, fortified margarine or other spread, dried milk powder, or perhaps a malted bedtime drink. The list of ingredients shows you which vitamins have been added and by comparing it with the Nutritional Information on the food label, you can see whether any of the vitamins occur naturally in the product or whether they have all been added. Typically, you might find the following list of vitamins in breakfast cereal: thiamin (B_1), riboflavin (B_2), niacin (B_3), B_6, folic acid (B_9), B_{12}. The malted bedtime drink might also have vitamins A, D, E, and C added to it.

(b) You may have chosen any of the vitamins. This answer looks at thiamin (B_1) and vitamin A.

According to the cereal packet, a 40 g serving of the cereal, with semi-skimmed milk, provides 0.4 mg of thiamin, which is said to be 30% of the RDA. (You will notice that, as mentioned before, this does not agree with the RNI value for thiamin given in Table SP9.1.) Many other common foods, such as pork, vegetables, milk, cheese, peas, fresh and dried fruit, eggs and wholegrain bread also contain thiamin. So, if you ate a selection of these foods, you would take in enough thiamin to reach the daily amount required (either the RNI or the RDA value).

According to the malted drink label, a serving provides 160 µg of vitamin A which is said to be 20% of the RDA. Vitamin A is also present in milk, cheese, eggs, yoghurt and fortified margarine, as well as oily fish (such as mackerel) and liver. Most people are therefore likely to take in sufficient vitamin A from some of these sources.

STUDY
PERIOD **18**

Public health nutrition and health promotion

18.1 Introduction

HN Chapter 18 provides an overview of the links between improving health by improving nutrition and looks at some of the ways in which healthy eating can be encouraged, and the challenges in getting these widely adopted.

18.2 Health and nutrition

You should finish your study of HN by reading all of Chapter 18 pp. 380–394.

Question SP18.1 (a) From HN Table 18.1, summarise the list of factors in the 'Dietary lack' column whose deficiency is linked to the various diseases identified, putting them into appropriate groupings where possible.

(b) Which of these factors would be covered by a diet that contained two portions of oily fish per week and five daily portions of a range of fruit and vegetables? ◀

Question SP18.2 The following questions test your understanding of HN Table 18.2 p. 384.

(a) What is the definition of PAL and what is signified by PAL > 1.75? You may find it useful to look back to SP15.3.

(b) Comment on the 'population goal' for *n*-3 PUFAs compared with those for the other fatty acids and suggest a possible reason for the difference.

(c) Use the information from HN p. 52, to identify how many standard 'units' of alcohol (in the UK) are equivalent to the optimum daily intake of alcohol.

(d) Explain the two different units that are given for the daily intake values of dietary fibre.

(e) The values for consumption of fruit and vegetables and for folate are both given in the table as > 400. How do the values actually compare? ◀

Question SP18.3 (a) Why might it be better to target whole populations than individuals with healthy eating advice?

(b) What is the difference between dietary advice that is nutrient-based and advice that is food-based? ◀

Summary of SP18

1 Since there are recognised links between diet and a number of health conditions, providing dietary advice could improve the health in a population.

2 Scientific advice giving optimum level of nutrients, etc. must be translated into a form in which it is accessible to the general population.

3 Producing a change in eating habits is not easy to do and advice must be reasonable, practical and compelling.

4 Different messages may be needed for different groups within the population.

And finally …

Now would be a good time to have a final look through the press articles and leaflets that you have been collecting to see how your study of this course has helped you to understand their accuracy, or otherwise. Do you now feel more confident about what constitutes a healthy diet and why?

Happy – and healthy – eating!

Answers to questions

Question SP1.1

(a) Since so many people in the UK are concerned about being overweight and are looking for quick and easy ways to lose weight, this article would probably cause great interest and large numbers of people might decide to try out the method.

(b) This method of weight loss might work because people on it would eat less food overall.

(c) The article could be dangerous because people following its advice might eat only a very limited range of nutrients, rather than the range required for a 'balanced diet'.

Question SP1.2

The ways in which data can be collected for each group is as follows:

(a) Populations:

By estimating the amount of food produced and consumed wholly within the country. A measure of the amount of food entering and leaving the country would also be needed.

By using data from supermarket tills and other food outlets, to identify the amount of food bought by the whole population.

(b) Families:

By checking the supermarket till receipts. Such data would not include those meals that were eaten outside the home, or food that was home-grown or purchased from outlets other than supermarkets.

By asking family members to keep a diary, or asking one member to keep a diary for all of them. Food diaries are notoriously unreliable, as people generally underestimate the amount that they eat.

(c) Individuals:

By keeping a food diary, though this approach has the problem of underestimation as in (b) above.

By weighing and recording all the food eaten. Such procedures are time-consuming and again may be unreliable with individuals 'forgetting' to weigh all their food or eating differently from normal during the period of study.

By using food-frequency questionnaires. Different portion sizes can make this unreliable.

Dietary interviews. People may not remember accurately what they have eaten.

Question SP1.3

(a) To convert her weight to kg:

10 stones = 10 × 6.35 kg = 63.5 kg

6 lbs = 6 × 0.45 kg = 2.7 kg

So her weight = 63.5 kg + 2.7 kg = 66.2 kg = 66 kg to the nearest whole kg.

To convert her height to m:

5 ft = 5 × 0.305 m = 1.525 m

9 inches = 9 × 0.025 m = 0.225 m

So her height = 1.525 m + 0.225 m = 1.75 m to the nearest cm.

(b) $$\text{BMI} = \frac{\text{weight in kg}}{(\text{height in m})^2}$$

$$= \frac{66}{(1.75)^2} = \frac{66}{1.75 \times 1.75} = 21.551$$

BMI values are often given to one decimal place, so this person's BMI would be 21.6, which is within the desirable range of 20–25 given at the top of HN p.12.

Question SP2.1

Statements (b) and (c) are correct; statements (a), (d) and (e) are false.

(a) Although bacteria do help with digestion of plant material, very few are found in the human stomach. So the correct version should be 'Bacteria in the *large intestine* help with the digestion of plant material'.

(d) Enzymes are released to digest food, but not from the wall of the large intestine. The correct version should be 'Enzymes are released from the walls of the *stomach and small intestine* and digest the food;

(e) 50% means 50 out of 100 and is the same as one-half, so it is not correct to say that more than 50% of the faeces is made up of bacteria. The correct version should be '*Up to* 50% of the dry weight of the faeces is made up of bacteria'.

Question SP2.2

(a) The macronutrients are protein, carbohydrates and fat. The micronutrients are vitamins and minerals.

(b) The list is: throat (pharynx), oesophagus, stomach, small intestine (duodenum, jejunum, ileum), large intestine (caecum, colon, rectum), anus.

Question SP2.3

The reasons you might have chosen are:

- We eat to stay alive.
- We eat because we are hungry.
- Eating is a 'habit' and food is widely available at any time.
- There are 'mealtimes' when people eat, and you are expected to eat at those times, whether or not you are hungry, i.e. eating is a social activity.
- Eating is enjoyable.
- People may eat for psychological reasons.

Question SP2.4

(a) A child arrives at school with his/her own preferences and habits learned from their mother and other people who have looked after them. These influences on diet will be affected by other children, school meals, other food sold at school (from a shop or from vending machines) and formal teaching about food and nutrition in lessons.

(b) The increase in the number of women in employment means that fewer of them regularly have time to prepare meals from basic ingredients. With so many ready-prepared convenience foods available from the freezer, ready to be heated in the microwave, each member of the family (including quite small children) can prepare their own meals very quickly and at a time convenient to them. Also about a third of meals are likely to be eaten outside the home, where all members of the family are unlikely to be present.

(c) Such magazines are likely to support the idea that to be attractive and healthy, young women should be thin. This attitude could encourage teenagers to eat less than is healthy and may result in other disadvantageous changes to their food intake. Advice on losing weight ('dieting') is also often given. Advertisements for various foods may also change their food choices and the magazines may contain recipes for interesting dishes.

(d) Younger people, those with lower incomes, and smokers have been found to be less likely to adopt dietary changes that would lead to more healthy eating.

Question SP2.5

(a) A person's choice of food is mainly determined by what is available to them (availability) and what they personally like to eat (acceptability).

(b) In rural areas in developing countries, the population is much more dependent on food that can be grown locally and is available in local markets. Due to the ease of transport and availability of food preservation methods, and the presence of large supermarkets, residents in large cities generally have a much wider choice of food.

(c) There are laws on:
- quality of food and lack of adulteration
- agricultural and trade policy (EU)
- food labelling
- irradiated food
- genetically engineered (modified) food
- foods containing synthetic substitutes.

(d) The average person in Britain spent 9.5% (just under one-tenth) of their budget on food in 2000.

Question SP2.6

(a) The five groups and their categories are:
- cereal/roots (starchy) foods – core food
- fruit and vegetables – secondary food
- meat and meat substitutes – secondary food
- milk and dairy produce – secondary food
- fatty and sugary foods – peripheral food.

(b) Appetite can be affected by the choice of food available. If people are not provided with the foods that they would choose to eat normally, that may have a major effect on how much they eat, which, of course, affects their speed of recovery.

(c) People may dislike the killing of animals and the methods used. They may have concerns about the conditions under which animals for food are reared. They may have concerns about the safety of some types of animal food (BSE in beef, *Salmonella* in eggs, etc.). They may have religious reasons for not eating meat.

(d) Single men may often eat alone and eat what they choose, which may not be a balanced diet. They may eat more ready-prepared and convenience foods. Women generally eat more 'healthy' foods (fruit and vegetables) and since they generally remain in charge of shopping and food preparation in the home, they may impose 'healthier' ways of eating on their husbands.

Question SP3.1

'Epidemiology' is the study of the occurrence of features of health and disease in whole populations, using statistical methods (*Glossary* definition). So in this context, large numbers of people whose diet is based largely on plant foods have been studied and their 'healthiness' has been measured (for example, by interview, by distributing questionnaires, or perhaps by using their medical records) and their lifespan recorded. Then these results are compared with those from a similar group of people (in the same area, or country, born around the same time, etc.) whose diet contains more meat-based foods. The evidence showed that, where both groups had enough food, then those eating mostly plant-based foods were healthier and lived longer. It's important to note that epidemiological studies apply only to whole populations and not to individuals.

Question SP3.2

The following appear in both lists:
- Eat the right amount to be a healthy weight/Aim for a healthy weight.
- Don't eat too much fat/Choose a diet that is low in saturated fat and cholesterol and moderate in total fat.
- Don't eat sugary foods too often/Choose beverages and foods that moderate your intake of sugars.
- If you drink, keep within sensible limits/If you drink alcoholic beverages, do so in moderation.

These guidelines appear only in the UK list:
- Enjoy your food.
- Eat a variety of different foods.
- Eat plenty of foods rich in starch and fibre.
- Look after the minerals and vitamins in your food.

These guidelines appear only in the USA list:
- Be physically active each day.
- Let the pyramid guide your food choices.
- Eat a variety of grains daily, especially whole grains.
- Eat a variety of fruits and vegetables daily.
- Keep foods safe to eat.
- Choose and prepare foods with less salt.

Some points of comparison are as follows:

The UK list starts with an exhortation to 'Enjoy your food'. It could be argued that choosing your diet on which foods were enjoyable might lead some people away from a healthy diet. The USA list gives more detailed advice on types of food – grains, fruit and vegetables. The UK list assumes that readers know which foods are rich in starch and fibre.

Both lists assume significant background knowledge. For example, the UK list contains 'look after the vitamins and minerals in your food' and the USA list mentions a 'pyramid' of foods.

Only the USA list mentions exercise and the importance of reducing salt, perhaps because the incidence of coronary heart disease is greater in the USA than the UK and these factors appear to be linked to coronary heart disease. We will come back to this later in the course.

You may have noted a variety of other points here that are equally valid.

Question SP3.3

The physiological nutrient requirement is the amount of a particular nutrient required each day to avoid signs of a deficiency.

The problems with this definition are:

- The amount can vary between individuals, depending on age, body mass, etc.
- For one person, it can vary from day to day, e.g. more energy-giving food might be required on some days than others.
- It can also vary depending on the composition of the total diet, which may affect how well particular nutrients are absorbed or used.
- If the definition gives the minimum amount required, then there is no safety margin. Some nutrients can be stored for later use, others cannot.
- It does not take account of nutrients for which it is not yet possible to recognise when the person is seriously short of that nutrient (i.e. a nutrient for which there are no signs of clinical deficiency).
- Even if there are signs of clinical deficiency, it is usually impossible to recognise a particular point at which that deficiency begins.

Question SP3.4

(a) The nutrient intake that provides sufficient for half the population but not the other half, i.e. the central value on the curve in HN Figure 3.2, is called the estimated average requirement or EAR.

(b) This value is used for energy intake because it would be undesirable to advise everyone to take in more than the average amount of energy in their diet, and risk a rise in obesity. On the other hand, if the EAR was used for nutrients such as vitamins, then half the population would be consuming less than they needed.

(c) Some people in any population need more than the EAR and some need less. Each individual should eat according to their appetite, rather than eating the amount of the EAR. However, taken over the whole population the EAR will be the average amount needed.

Question SP3.5

(a) Food manufacturers use the term recommended daily amount (RDA).

(b) The new name for the RDA is the 'recommended nutrient intake' or RNI, also often referred to as the dietary reference value (DRV).

(c) If people consumed the RNI for a particular vitamin, only 2.5% of the population would not be getting enough. The part of the graph between the lower reference nutrient intake LRNI (point D on HN Figure 3.2) and the RNI (point C on HN Figure 3.2) covers 95% of the population, leaving 2.5% below the LRNI and 2.5% above the RNI. The people below the LRNI would be getting more than enough of the vitamin, so only the 2.5% above the RNI would be getting insufficient.

Question SP3.6

The picture represents a plate, divided into segments, each containing pictures of examples of foods belonging to a particular food group. Five groups are shown: meat, fish and alternatives; fruit and vegetables; bread, other cereals and potatoes; milk and dairy foods; and foods containing fat and/or sugar (grouped together). The size of the segment of the plate indicates how much of each of the various groups of food should be present in the diet. The fruit and vegetables segment and the bread, other cereals and potatoes segment each occupy one-third of the plate. The remaining one-third is divided into three sections, with the smallest section being the foods containing fat and sugar, so these should make up only a small proportion of your diet. The meat, fish and alternatives segment and milk and dairy foods segment make up, in about equal amounts, the remainder of that third of the plate. A healthy balanced diet for a typical adult, averaged out over a number of meals, should contain items from these food groups in these proportions.

(You might like to try out your answer, or this answer, on a friend to see if it gets the message across.)

Question SP4.1

(a) The four interactions are:

- Hydrophobic interactions. Those R groups that attract water molecules mostly lie on the outside of the folded protein; those that do not interact with water are clustered together on the inside of the folded chain.

- Ionic interactions. Some amino acids have charged R groups, which attract oppositely charged R groups and repel those with like charges.

- Hydrogen bonds. Depend on partial charges. They occur between H attached to O or N, and O or N elsewhere in the polypeptide chain or in a different chain.

- Disulfide bridges. Occur between the sulfur atoms in the R groups of cysteine molecules in different parts of the same polypeptide chain, or in different chains.

(b) If the change in the amino acid was from one with a hydrophobic R group to one with a hydrophilic R group (or vice versa), then it could cause the protein chain to fold differently. Similarly, if the change in the amino acid produced a change in the charge of the R group, then this could affect the ionic interactions and could affect the folding. Since hydrogen bonding can occur between R groups, a change could affect those interactions too, and thus affect folding. Disulfide bridges occur only between cysteines, so if the change involved a cysteine, then the folding would be affected, whereas if not, the disulfide bridges would remain unchanged. (SP4.6.2 looks at a protein that is affected in a major way by a single amino acid change.)

Question SP4.2

(a) RNI for a female aged 40 is 45.0 g of protein per day. So the daily intake of protein is 71.3 g − 45.0 g = 26.3 g greater than the reference nutrient intake.

(b) Expressed as a percentage of RNI, this value would be

$$\frac{26.3\,\text{g}}{45.0\,\text{g}} \times 100\% = 58.4\%$$

So the average daily intake of protein is over half as much again as the reference nutrient intake for a female aged 40.

Question SP4.3

(a) The safe limit for protein intake for a 60 kg woman would be 60 × 1.5 g protein per day = 90 g.

(b) The estimated average requirement EAR is only 36 g per day. So, the safe limit is $\dfrac{90}{36}$ times greater = 2.5 (or two and a half) times greater than the estimated average requirement.

(c) Table SP4.2 shows that lean beef is 20% protein. So, a 250 g steak contains $\dfrac{20}{100} \times 250$ g protein = 50 g protein. So this alone does not exceed the safe limit for protein, though for other reasons it might not be the ideal basis for a healthy diet, and of course, significant amounts of protein would be consumed in other foods during the day.

Question SP5.1

Here is a list of some fats and oils. You may have thought of others.

Fats	Oils
butter	vegetable oil
soft margarine	sunflower oil
hard margarine	olive oil
lard	groundnut oil
dripping	cod liver oil
suet	sesame oil
	corn oil
	peanut oil
	walnut oil

Question SP5.2

(a) The saturated fatty acid that occurs in all the foods listed in the largest quantities has 18 carbon atoms and, from Table SP5.1, is stearic acid.

(b) The most common fatty acid in each group has 18 carbon atoms – stearic acid in the saturates, oleic acid in the monounsaturates and linoleic and linolenic acids in the polyunsaturated group.

(c) The two tallest blue columns (measuring approximately to the 50% mark) correspond to corn oil and soft margarine. It is not possible to identify whether this fatty acid is linoleic or linolenic acid, or a mixture.

(d) Hard fats contain more saturated fatty acids and oils contain more poly-unsaturated ones. Both groups contain significant quantities of monounsaturated fatty acids.

Question SP5.3

(a) You should have circled the vertical row of carbons with their hydrogen atoms on the left of each of the triacylglycerols, together with the oxygen atom next to each of them.

(b) Molecule (a) contains two palmitic acid (16 C) tails and one stearic acid (18 C) tail. Molecule (b) has three different fatty acids – one palmitic acid, one stearic acid and one arachidic (20 C) acid.

Question SP5.4

(a) The melting temperature decreases from front to back. Cod liver oil, olive oil and corn oil are all liquid at room temperature. Butter and margarine may soften at room temperature but need to be heated above room temperature to melt them completely. Beef fat and lard remain solid at room temperature and melt at a higher temperature than butter and margarine.

(b) There are more polyunsaturated fatty acids in the oils (at the back of the diagram) which have the lower melting temperatures, and fewer polyunsaturated fatty acids in the hard fats (at the front of the diagram) with the higher melting temperatures.

(c) Fatty acids with more double bonds have bends in the chains of carbon atoms, so the molecules pack less closely, so the forces holding the molecules together will be weaker. These fatty acids occur in the oils with the lower melting temperatures. The hard fats at the front of the diagram contain fewer polyunsaturated fatty acids and more saturated fatty acids. Saturated fatty acids, without any double bonds, pack more neatly together, the forces holding them together are stronger and so the melting temperature of fats containing them is higher.

Question SP5.5

At a temperature of about 4 °C (fridge temperature), most of the triacylglycerols in butter are below their melting temperature, so they are solid. At room temperature, about 20 °C, some of the triacylglycerols are above their melting temperature and so the butter is softer and spreads easily. Soft margarine spreads straight from the fridge, so some of its triacylglycerols must have melting temperatures below 4 °C; otherwise it would be hard at that temperature. Since its texture changes very little at room temperature, the remaining triacylglycerols must have melting temperatures above 20 °C, so that it remains spreadable, rather than becoming a liquid, over this large temperature range.

Question SP5.6

(a) False. Only phospholipids and cholesterol are important lipid components of cell membranes. Lipoproteins are not.

(b) True.

(c) False. Triacylglycerols are hydrophobic and therefore do not mix with blood unless they are attached to protein molecules, as lipoproteins.

(d) False. The reverse is true. LDLs contain proportionately more cholesterol than VLDLs.

(e) False. The risk factor for coronary heart disease depends on the relative proportions of LDL and HDL cholesterol. High HDL cholesterol levels compared with LDL levels are linked with a lower risk of CHD.

Question SP6.1

(a) The statement is false. In glucose the ring is composed of five carbon atoms and one oxygen, but in fructose there are only four carbon atoms and one oxygen in the ring. The ring is a pentagon (five sides), rather than a hexagon (six sides).

(b) A careful count of the atoms in the two molecules, remembering to count the numbered carbon atoms at the 'corners', shows that the molecules both contain six carbon atoms, 12 hydrogen atoms and six oxygen atoms. They both have the molecular formula $C_6H_{12}O_6$ and so the statement is true.

Question SP6.2

Table SP6.3 is an example of a summary table for dietary carbohydrates. Note that glycogen is not included as very little is actually eaten.

Table SP6.3 The main carbohydrates in the diet.

MONOSACCHARIDES	DISACCHARIDES	POLYSACCHARIDES
galactose → lactose		Starch (amylose + amylopectin)
glucose → maltose		cellulose
fructose → sucrose		NSPs

Question SP6.3

Your completed Table SP6.1 should look like Table SP6.4.

Table SP6.4 Completed Table SP6.1. Carbohydrate digestion in the small intestine.

Enzyme	Substance being digested	Products of digestion
dextrinase	dextrins	glucose
lactase	lactose	glucose and galactose
maltase	maltose	glucose
sucrase	sucrose	glucose and fructose

Question SP7.1

(a) It is possible to make a good estimate since 150 g of yoghurt provides 156 kcal, then 1 g contains just over 1 kcal and so 100 g contains just over 100 kcal. Using a calculator gives 1 g containing $\frac{156}{150}$ kcal = 1.04 kcal, so 100 g contains 104 kcal.

Since nutritional information on food labels is usually given per 100 g, as well as per serving, this value can also be found on the yoghurt pot.

(b) The first step is to convert 156 kcal to kJ, knowing that 1 kcal = 4.2 kJ.

So 156 kcal is equivalent to 156 × 4.2 kJ = 655.2 kJ.

In 150 g yoghurt, there are 655 kJ, so in 1 g yoghurt there are $\frac{655}{150}$ kJ = 4.37 kJ

So, the yoghurt contains 4 kJ per gram (to the nearest kJ).

Alternatively, you can use the value from (a) of 1.04 kcal per gram, and multiply by 4.2 to convert to kJ per gram. You should get the same answer.

Question SP7.2

6.3 g protein produces 6.3 × 4 kcal = 25.2 kcal.

26.1 g carbohydrate produces 26.1 × 4 kcal = 104.4 kcal.

2.9 g fat produces 2.9 × 9 kcal = 26.1 kcal.

Total energy produced = 25.2 kcal + 104.4 kcal + 26.1 kcal = 155.7 kcal, which, to the nearest whole kcal, is 156 kcal, as it says on the pot.

You can, of course, do similar calculations for yourself with foods of your choice.

Question SP7.3

Amount of gin = 50 g of which 40% is alcohol.

So, amount of alcohol = $\frac{40}{100}$ × 50 g = 20 g

Energy produced by alcohol = 29 kJ per gram, so for 20 g, that is a total of 20 × 29 kJ = 580 kJ. With the added tonic, the total energy intake is 580 + 198 kJ = 778 kJ.

In Question SP7.1b, it was calculated that the yoghurt contained 655 kJ, so the gin and tonic contains 778 − 655 kJ = 123 kJ more energy than the yoghurt.

Question SP8.1

You may have included some of the following in your lists:

Food: there is a much greater variety of tempting food now available in the UK; shopping is easier with supermarkets and internet shopping; most people earn sufficient money to buy plenty of food; there is much more convenience food available, both for eating at home and eating out; fewer people grow their own fruit and vegetables; high-energy snacks are easily available and regularly replace proper meals in some households.

Activity: motorised transport is much more easily available and few people now walk or cycle to work; many manual jobs have disappeared to be replaced by sedentary occupations; housework is much less demanding, with household appliances for cleaning, cooking, washing-up and washing; leisure time is often spent in sedentary activities, such as watching TV and playing video games, rather than taking part in active sports.

Question SP8.2

Table SP8.3 Completed version of Table SP8.2 Obesity in the UK population in 1980 and 2001, with estimates for 2020.

Year	Obesity in various groups in the UK population/%					
	All adults	Men	Women	All children	6-year-olds	15-year-olds
1980		6	8			
2001		21	25		9	15
2020	33			50		

(a) The statement that 'obesity has increased by three times in the past 20 years' appears to be something of an underestimate for men between 1980 and 2001. Obesity has increased from 6% to 21%, which is 3.5 times. Obesity in women has risen just slightly more than three times, from 8% to 25%. So, taking men and women together, an increase of three times in obesity in adults is reasonably accurate. Assuming that obesity percentages increased steadily from 1980 to 2001 and have continued to increase until the current year, then the statement is probably an underestimate.

(b) Obesity in children is predicted to be 50% by 2020. So, to increase by three times, it would need to have been at a level of about 17% (50/3) in 2001. We do not have the full set of data for all children in 2001, but it would be surprising if the average percentage of obesity in all children in 2001 did not lie between the 9% value for 6-year-olds and the 15% value for 15-year-olds. If we take that value to be around 12%, then the prediction is that obesity in children could increase by four times. Of course, if current Government health initiatives have the desired effect, it is hoped that not only will the incidence of obesity in children not increase at all, but that it will show a distinct decline.

Question SP8.3

(a) These BMI values have been given with their units, i.e. kg/m^2, whereas usually units are not included with BMI values.

(b) People with a BMI of 27 or more (paragraph 1.1.1) would be classified as overweight (the overweight range is 25–30). Those with a BMI of 30 or more (paragraph 1.1.2) would be classified as obese or severely obese.

(c) People under the age of 18 or over the age of 65 should not be prescribed the drug. People who do not have any other conditions or diseases cannot be prescribed the drug unless their BMI is 30 or more. People who have not made any serious attempts to lose weight by other means are also excluded from receiving the drug.

(d) Since the drug can only be prescribed if there are 'adequate arrangements for monitoring … adverse effects', it would appear that doctors do not expect the drug to be free of side-effects.

Question SP9.1

(a) Vitamin C is needed in the greatest amount, namely 40 mg per day.

(b) The other vitamins needed by men in quantities of more than 1 mg per day are vitamin E and the B vitamins, i.e. thiamin, riboflavin, niacin and vitamin B_6

(c) 100 μg is 0.1 mg, so vitamins needed in less than this quantity are vitamin D (10 μg for certain groups of people), vitamin K (about 70 μg), vitamin B_{12} (1.5 μg) and biotin (between 10 μg and 200 μg needed).

Question SP9.2

(a) RDA is the recommended daily allowance, so the values in the third column are the percentage of that amount that would be obtained from a bowl of this cereal with milk.

(b) Knowing that 0.4 mg of thiamin represents 30% of the RDA, then the task is to calculate 100% of the RDA.

If 30% RDA = 0.4 mg, then 1% is $\dfrac{0.4}{30}$ mg and 100% is $\dfrac{0.4}{30} \times 100$ mg = 1.3 mg. So the RDA of thiamin is 1.3 mg.

Table SP9.1 gives an RNI value for thiamin of 0.8 mg for women and 1 mg for men, so the value quoted on the cereal packet is significantly greater. The reasons for the discrepancies are unclear. It could be that the recommended daily amount of thiamin has been reduced recently, and the cereal packet information has not been updated. It may be that the cereal manufacturer is using USA rather than UK values, which may be different. Or it may be a simple error in a calculation somewhere.

If you did similar calculations for the other vitamins, you would discover similar discrepancies, though sometimes the RDA values on the cereal packet are greater and sometimes smaller than the values in Table SP9.1. This example illustrates the problems with numerical, and other, information in the nutrition area. It is often very difficult to know how much reliance to place on a particular set of figures, or on particular information.

(c) Thiamin, riboflavin, vitamin B_6 and vitamin B_{12} are likely to be present in both the cereal and the milk. Folic acid is probably present only in the cereal. Niacin appears to be present only in the milk.

Question SP9.3

Eggs appear as a source of nine of the 13 vitamins. Only vitamins E, K, folate (vitamin B_9) and C are absent. Eggs are the food source for the developing chick and, as such, must contain all the substances needed to build its body, amongst which are the vitamins. For similar reasons, milk is also rich in vitamins.

Question SP9.4

Some chemical reactions in the body produce harmful substances called free radicals that contain single electrons and become involved in chain reactions in the cells, which can be damaging to the body. Antioxidants like vitamins A and E neutralise the harmful substances and prevent further damage.

Question SP9.5

Table SP9.1 indicates that 40 mg of vitamin C are needed each day.
Assume that the person has an average amount of 2.5 g, or 2500 mg of vitamin C in their body. For scurvy to develop, vitamin C reserves would need to fall below 300 mg, so 2500 mg − 300 mg = 2200 mg would need to be used and not replaced from the diet. At the rate of 40 mg per day, scurvy would appear after $\dfrac{2200}{40}$ days = 55 days, i.e. in less than 2 months (assuming no vitamin C is available from the diet).

Question SP9.6

(a) Any of the water-soluble vitamins could be lost in the water that drips from the thawed beef. The water-soluble vitamins found in beef are niacin (vitamin B_3) and some vitamin B_{12} and pantothenic acid (vitamin B_5).

(b) The fat-soluble vitamins could be lost in the fat that drips from the meat during cooking but beef contains very few of the fat-soluble vitamins, just perhaps a small amount of vitamin K.

Question SP9.7

(a) Vitamin D can be made in the skin, provided that it is exposed to sufficient sunlight. Vitamin A can be made from β-carotene in the diet, obtained from carrots and from dark green leafy vegetables. Niacin (vitamin B_3) can be made from the amino acid tryptophan.

(b) Vitamins A, E and K are groups of compounds, as is the vitamin B complex, though the members of this group are given separate names.

(c) Vitamins A, C and E are the vitamins that act as antioxidants. Vitamin A can be made from β-carotene (see above), but the others must be obtained through the diet.

Question SP9.8
Table SP9.3 The similarities between some pairs of vitamins.

Vitamins	Sources	Functions	Signs of deficiency
(a) riboflavin and niacin	both found in milk and eggs	both involved in cell metabolism	both affect the skin – riboflavin deficiency causes cracks around the mouth, etc. – niacin deficiency causes dermatitis (one of the symptoms of pellagra)
(b) folate and vitamin B_{12}	both found in yeast extract and breakfast cereals	both important in cell division	both deficiencies result in anaemia – folate linked to megaloblastic anaemia – vitamin B_{12} to pernicious anaemia
(c) vitamins E and C	both found in some vegetables	both act as antioxidants by destroying free radicals	no clear symptoms related to vitamin E – lack of vitamin C causes scurvy.

Question SP9.9

A bowl of cereal with milk at breakfast time, together with eggs sometimes and fresh fruit regularly eaten at other meals would provide a good source of almost all the vitamins. Additionally introducing some fresh, easy to prepare vegetables, such as broccoli, into their diet would be beneficial.

Question SP10.1

(a) The two elements with the highest reference nutrient intake (RNI) values are potassium (3.5 g) and chlorine (2.5 g).

(b) The two elements that occur in the largest amounts in the body are calcium (1000 g or 1 kg) and phosphorus (700 g). The one in the list that occurs in the smallest amounts is magnesium (though there are many more elements that are present in even smaller quantities in the body as you will see later).

Question SP10.2

(a) Since the salt content is 2.5 times higher than the sodium content, 100 g of the cereal contains 0.3×2.5 g salt $= 0.75$ g salt, while 100 g of the ready-made meal contains 0.4×2.5 g salt $= 1$ g of salt.

(b) Since 100 g of the cereal contains 0.75 g salt, 1 g of cereal contains $\dfrac{0.75}{100}$ g salt and so a 40 g portion contains $40 \times \dfrac{0.75}{100}$ g salt $= 0.3$ g salt.

And similarly, since 100 g of the ready-made meal contains 1 g of salt, 1 g of the meal contains $\dfrac{1}{100}$ g salt and the whole of the 450 g portion would contain

$450 \times \dfrac{1}{100}$ g salt $= 4.5$ g salt.

(c) The advised daily intake for a woman is 5 g per day. The ready-made meal contains 90% ($\dfrac{4.5\,g}{5\,g} \times 100\% = 90\%$) of this quantity, while a portion of the cereal contains only 6% ($\dfrac{0.3\,g}{5\,g} \times 100\% = 6\%$). However, a bowl of cereal for breakfast and the chicken curry later in the day, would provide almost all of the woman's recommended salt intake for the day.

Question SP10.3

(a) The total amount of iron in her body is 60×40 mg $= 2400$ mg $= 2.4$ g. This quantity is significantly less than the average amount of iron in the human body which is usually given as 4 g. Women of reproductive age are often short of iron due to menstrual losses or to the needs of pregnancy.

(b) If two-thirds of this quantity is in the haemoglobin, then the amount of iron in the haemoglobin is

2.4 g $\times \dfrac{2}{3} = 1.6$ g, i.e. just over one and a half grams.

Question SP10.4

The values for mineral water are all far below the limits given and, in fact, mineral water appears to be rather low in minerals, compared with the limits permissible in drinking water. The bicarbonate in the mineral water is produced by the dissolved carbon dioxide and this also lowers the pH value.

Question SP11.1

Here is a possible answer, written in about 210 words:

If she has a BMI less than 20.8 (the threshold for normal pregnancy), she should attempt to gain some weight by eating a high-calorie diet to increase her chances of becoming pregnant. If she is overweight, she should attempt to reduce her BMI to within the normal range.

She should ensure that she eats a balanced, mixed diet, containing plenty of protein. Micronutrients are important for the mother's health too, especially vitamin B_{12}, iodine, magnesium and zinc. Folic acid is particularly important in reducing the occurrence of neural tube defects (such as spina bifida) (see SP9.6.5) and she would be well advised to take folic acid supplements. She should avoid eating liver and liver products, such as pâté, because the large doses of vitamin A (retinol) that may be present can cause malformations in the developing baby. Similarly any dietary supplements containing retinol should be avoided. She should restrict her alcohol intake to no more than one drink (1–2 units) per day, since alcohol is also teratogenic, and her partner should similarly reduce his alcohol intake, since drinking heavily can reduce the sperm count. Monounsaturated and polyunsaturated fats, together with riboflavin and vitamins C and E, can protect against genetic defects in the developing fetus, so fresh fruit and raw vegetables are recommended too.

Question SP11.2

(a) Vitamin A – Table SP9.1 indicates that vitamin A is found in liver, cheese, eggs, butter, oily fish (such as mackerel), milk, fortified margarine and yoghurt, but does not mention fruit and vegetables. However, SP9.2 states that vitamin A can be synthesised in the body from β-carotene, found in cabbage, sprouts, broccoli, spinach, and carrots. So, eating extra vegetables should increase the vitamin A intake; eating extra fruit would not provide much additional vitamin A.

Vitamin C – This is found in a wide variety of fruit and vegetables, especially peppers, broccoli, sprouts, sweet potatoes, cranberries, citrus fruits and kiwi fruit (Table SP9.1), so the advice is accurate here.

Riboflavin – Also known as vitamin B_2, riboflavin is found in milk, eggs, fortified breakfast cereals, rice and mushrooms. Only mushrooms fall into the 'fruit and vegetables' category here.

Folate – Folate (or folic acid, sometimes called vitamin B_9) occurs in broccoli, sprouts, peas, chick peas, yeast extract, brown rice, some fruit (such as oranges and bananas), breakfast cereals and some bread. So increasing general fruit and vegetable consumption should increase folate intake.

Vitamin D – Like vitamin A, this vitamin is fat-soluble and is found in greatest quantities in oily fish, liver and eggs, margarine, breakfast cereals, bread and powdered milk, but not in significant quantities in fruit and vegetables.

So the statement in HN Figure 11.3 would probably have been better not to include fruits and vegetables as a source of vitamin D and only mushrooms provide much riboflavin. Otherwise the statement is accurate.

(b) Under normal circumstances, it is not necessary to include vitamin D in the diet since it can be synthesised in the skin during the summer in sufficient quantities to last through the winter months. Between October and March in the UK, there is not enough UV-B in sunlight for adequate synthesis to occur. Vitamin D has a role in the metabolism of calcium and the development of bones, and there is an increased requirement for it during pregnancy when the skeleton of the fetus is forming. So, if a woman is pregnant during the winter, vitamin D supplements may be necessary to keep levels high enough in the body, especially if the woman is on a vegetarian diet.

Question SP11.3

Fetal programming is the process by which circumstances that occur during the development of a fetus in the womb can have consequences for the health of that person for the rest of their life.

Question SP11.4

Babies who have a low birthweight are thought to be more likely, as adults, to suffer from:

- high blood pressure
- insulin resistance and Type 2 diabetes
- poor cholesterol metabolism and increased likelihood of blood clotting
- coronary heart disease (CHD) linked to the above

Question SP11.5

When the baby begins to suck, the hypothalamus in the mother's brain is stimulated via nerves that run from the nipple to the brain (not shown in this diagram.) The hypothalamus stimulates the pituitary gland which is attached to the underneath of the brain, and causes it to produce two important substances (hormones) called prolactin and oxytocin. However, if the mother is apprehensive, tired or tense, this release can be inhibited. Prolactin, from the anterior pituitary gland, stimulates milk production in the breast. Milk contains fats and sugars (and other components too that are not shown). Fats with short-chain fatty acids are produced in the breast. Long-chain fatty acids are brought in via the bloodstream. Glucose is also supplied in the blood and combined with galactose synthesised in the breast to form the sugar in milk that is called lactose. Oxytocin, from the posterior pituitary gland, stimulates the release (ejection) of the milk.

Question SP11.6

(a) She should take in additional calories and protein. She also needs more vitamin A, riboflavin, niacin, vitamin B_{12}, folate, vitamin C and vitamin D. She will need more calcium, magnesium and zinc.

(b) Milk in the human diet (assumed to be cows' milk) contains quantities of vitamin A, riboflavin, niacin and vitamin B_{12}. However, it does not contain significant quantities of folate or vitamins C or D. Milk is a source of calcium and magnesium, but may not contain much zinc. However, zinc is present in protein-rich foods, so by increasing her protein intake, she would probably increase her zinc intake too.

(c) If she ate some additional fruit, such as an orange, that would provide extra folate and vitamin C and an egg would provide vitamin D. You may have made other choices of food here, that are equally valid.

(d) While menstruating, a woman loses iron, in the haemoglobin molecules in blood, from her body each month. During pregnancy and while lactating, periods cease (called amenorrhoea) and so she may have sufficient iron reserves in her body to cope with the extra demands.

Question SP12.1

(a) In adults, all proteins are digested into amino acids and the amino acids are then absorbed into the bloodstream. In young infants, however, because their digestive system is less well developed, some proteins remain undigested and can be absorbed intact, rather than as individual amino acids, into the blood. This capacity is beneficial in enabling uptake of antibodies from their mother's milk. The antibodies help to prevent infections. However, if the infant is given other proteins, such as those in cows' milk or in egg white, then these may also pass unchanged into the infant's blood and can cause allergies in the child later in life.

(b) Proteins are needed for growth in infants and the milk should contain sufficient fat and carbohydrate (lactose) to prevent the protein being used for the production of energy. Too much protein can be harmful as excess amino acids are converted to urea which is then excreted in urine (SP4.7.2), removing water from the body. So there is a possibility that the baby could become dehydrated if the protein intake is too high.

Question SP12.2

(a) Between 6 and 9 months old, babies need about 95 kcal per kg of their body weight each day. So a baby girl weighing 8 kg would need 8×95 kcal of energy = 760 kcal each day.

(b) The columns headed EAR are calculated by multiplying the average body weight of the child by the energy requirement per kilogram of body weight. Boys do not need any more energy per kg of body weight, but their average body weight is greater than that of girls, so their total energy needs per day are more.

(c) You will have answered this question for your own situation. This example uses a female weighing 60 kg and in the age range 19–50 years. She needs 1940 kcal each day and so her energy requirement would be $\dfrac{1940}{60}$ kcal/kg body weight = about 32 kcal/kg body weight.

The energy requirement, from HN Table 12.2 for a 6 month old baby boy is 95 kcal/kg body weight, which is almost three times as much. Babies need relatively more energy because they have relatively more muscle (metabolically active tissue) than adults and are growing fast.

Question SP12.3

Long-chain fatty acids are those with 14 or more carbon atoms. The term n-3 indicates that the fatty acid has a double bond attached to the third carbon counting from the CH_3 end of the molecule. There are probably more double bonds too, which means that the fatty acid would be described as polyunsaturated. Suitable examples of n-3 fatty acids are (alpha) linolenic acid with 18 C atoms and three double bonds, eicosapentaenoic acid with 20 C atoms and five double bonds and docosahexaenoic acid with 22 C atoms and 6 double bonds. These fatty acids can all be referred to as omega 3, rather than n-3. (You should have found this information in SP5.3.4 and your completed Table SP5.1.)

Question SP12.4

Lactose and sucrose are both disaccharides, made by the linking together of two monosaccharides. In lactose the monosaccharides are glucose and galactose. In sucrose, glucose is again one of the components, but the other one is fructose. (SP6.3)

Question SP12.5

There is a rare condition in which lack of vitamin K is linked to bleeding into the brain in the first few weeks of life, causing serious brain damage. It occurs in about 1 in 10 000 babies and is completely prevented by a dose of vitamin K, either orally or injected, soon after birth. (SP9.5)

Question SP12.6

You might have chosen some of the following points:

Check that the breakfast cereal and the jars of baby food are fortified with iron and vitamin D. If not, switch to ones that are, since iron is essential for the production of haemoglobin in the blood and with insufficient, the child may become anaemic. Vitamin D prevents rickets and is important in normal bone growth.

Use full-fat or formula milk on the cereal, since it is important that the child obtains enough energy from her food for normal growth and development and the fat in milk is an energy-rich food.

Give her some vegetables and fruit, pureed if necessary, as part of her meals, since currently she is getting almost no vitamin C (a little may be present in the jars of baby food). Vitamin C is important in the formation of collagen, which is a crucial component of bones, tendons, cartilage and skin. It also helps in the absorption of iron.

Don't regularly give her foods high in sugar such as cake to avoid her developing a liking for sweet things. Dietary sugar is a major factor in tooth decay, so cut out the cake and replace it with fruit or yoghurt.

Offer your child different foods to try, since a wide range of foods in her diet will result in most of the essential nutrients being taken in.

Replace the sweetened orange drink with formula milk. A child of 9 months should be having 500–600 ml of milk each day, as milk is an important source of protein, calcium and vitamins, as well as energy.

The sweetened drink can also cause dental decay, so if extra drinks are needed, choose ones that are sugar-free and offer them in a cup.

Question SP12.7

(a) Children should have a balanced diet with a wide variety of foods and an appropriate balance between the five food groups – bread, cereals and potatoes (starchy foods); fruit and vegetables; meat, fish, etc., milk and dairy foods; and fatty and sugary foods. There should be five servings of the starchy foods and five of fruit and vegetables; three servings of milk and dairy foods and two servings from the meat group. Fatty and sugary foods should only be eaten in small quantities. (HN p. 268)

(b) Once children go to school, they have more opportunities to choose their own foods, although parents still have significant control over what is eaten at mealtimes at home and what snacks are available (HN p. 265). Children may reject foods as part of demonstrating their own independence. They may also be influenced by their peers and by advertising. (HN p. 266)

(c) Vitamins and minerals are the nutrients whose intake is most likely to be below the recommended levels. Vitamin A and riboflavin (vitamin B_2) intakes are often low (HN p. 270). Younger children tend to have low levels of intake of zinc, but in older children there is a wider range of minerals where the intake may be low, including iron, calcium, magnesium, potassium, zinc and iodine. (HN p. 270)

Question SP12.8

The four points of comparison are:

- The values for the percentage of energy in the diet provided by fat in both boys and girls aged 4 to 18 are within 1% of the general recommendation of 35%.

- Similarly the carbohydrate intakes are very close; the young people's intake (between 51% and 52%) is very slightly higher than the recommendation (50%).

- Since the total energy intake must be 100%, and energy comes from proteins, carbohydrates and fats in the diet, then the value for the energy intake for proteins, if it were given in HN Table 12.6 would be 15% (carbohydrate + fat = 50% + 35%). The young people's intake of 13% is just slightly lower.

- The general recommendation is for a non-starch polysaccharide intake of 18 g per day. The intake of the young people is less than this value, at just over 11 g for boys and nearly 10 g for girls.

Assuming that the food intake was reported accurately, these data would suggest that the diet of the 1700+ young people surveyed in the National Diet and Nutrition Survey published in 2000 was close to the national recommendations, though an increased intake of NSPs would be beneficial.

Question SP12.9

There is a wide range of topics from which to choose and the exact choice may depend on the area in which you live and the problems that you perceive as being most significant in the school. However, you would almost certainly cover:

- What constitutes a balanced diet
- The importance of vitamins and minerals

You might also cover:

- Keeping your body weight steady – the dangers of dieting and obesity
- Drinking and smoking
- Diet in pregnancy
- Being a vegetarian and other restricted diets
- Diet and sport.

Question SP13.1

(a) Why the diet of men may not be optimal:

- Although they know the risks of heart disease, they assume it will not happen to them and therefore do not alter their diet to reduce the intake of fat.

- Traditionally men expect to eat lots of meat and not so much fruit and vegetables.

- They are generally less concerned about their diet than women and less exposed to dietary information, both at school and thereafter.

- They are generally less concerned about body weight.

- Traditionally, they are more likely than women to adopt an unhealthy lifestyle, including smoking and drinking.

(b) Why the diet of women may not be optimal:

- They have a smaller overall intake than men and they may be at risk of insufficient intakes of micronutrients.
- Many adolescent girls have a desire to be slim and may suffer from osteoporosis in later life because of insufficient intake of minerals at this stage.
- Reproductive capability may also be jeopardised if the body does not contain a normal amount of fat, together with sufficient micronutrients (vitamins and minerals).
- Iron is lost during menstruation, and with insufficient iron intake, many women are anaemic.
- Although a woman may wish to eat a healthy diet, she may be influenced by her partner and children to eat a less healthy one.
- Poverty tends to lead to a less than optimal diet and more women live in poverty than men.

(c) Why the diet of vegetarians may not be optimal:

- Certain nutrients, especially vitamins and minerals, may be deficient if the range of food in the diet is limited.
- Iron intake is likely to be low, since it is less easily extracted from a vegetarian diet (poorer bioavailability).
- There may also be shortages of vitamin D and long-chain n-3 fatty acids.

Question SP13.2

Hindus are vegetarians, though they do eat dairy products. The vegetables they are familiar with may well be very different from UK vegetables. They may not know how to cook or serve those available to them in the UK, or they might prefer not to eat them, leading to them eating a rather restricted range from the 'fruit and vegetables' segment. They may not be able to obtain familiar bread, so may not eat an appropriate mix from the 'bread, other cereals and potatoes' segment. From the 'meat, fish and alternatives', they probably only eat pulses and nuts, and possibly eggs, though some Hindus, particularly women, avoid eggs. Their traditional diet would probably contain little from the 'food containing fat' and 'food containing sugar' segment but these might be eaten as a substitute for items they would choose but are unable to obtain in the UK, leading to a less well-balanced diet overall. As with many Asian immigrants, they may be short of vitamin D, though the inclusion of dairy products should supply some vitamin D in the diet.

Question SP13.3

Living on a low income may make it more difficult to eat healthily because:

- Local shops may have to be used, due to transport costs. These shops may charge higher prices for lower-quality products than an out-of-town supermarket.
- Cheaper foods are bought that have lower nutritional value. For example, cheaper meat products probably contain more fat and salt than more expensive ones. Cheaper vegetables may be less fresh and therefore their vitamin content will be lower.

- To avoid waste, parents may be more willing to give children their preferred foods, which may not be the best for them nutritionally. Such habits may also lead to a less varied diet, thereby risking shortage of certain micronutrients.

- Foods that are easy to prepare and serve, such as meat pies, may be chosen, which may contain less nutrients than a meal prepared at home, with meat, vegetables, etc.

- The cheapest way of eating a filling meal and one that provides sufficient energy, may be to eat foods that are high in fat and sugar, rather than those that contain more balanced nutrients.

Question SP13.4

Follow basic healthy eating guidelines relating to fat, fibre, sugar and salt by using the Balance of Good Health – Eating foods in the same proportions that are shown on The Balance of Good Health 'plate' (Figure SP3.2) ensures suitable relative quantities of the various foods in the diet (The plate provides no direct information on salt intake, which should be restricted to 5 g for women and 7 g for men (SP10.2.5)).

Recognise that snacks can be an important part of the diet – Older people have smaller appetites and may not eat sufficient at mealtimes to meet all their nutritional requirements. Suitable snacks can help to make up any shortage.

Make sure that fluid intakes are adequate – Kidney function declines in older people and they may not recognise that they are thirsty. A fluid intake of about 1.5–2 litres per day is recommended (HN p. 295).

Keep some food stocks in the house for emergencies – This precaution is sensible in the case of bad weather or if the person does not feel well enough to go shopping.

Try to spend some time outdoors, especially in the spring and summer – Vitamin D, important in maintaining bone density, can be manufactured in the skin in sunlight (SP9.3).

If alone, try to arrange to share meals with friends/neighbours – Loneliness may lead to depression and to a lack of appetite (HN Figure 13.2 p. 294). When food is shared and meals are eaten in company, food intake is increased (HN p. 297)

Ask for help with shopping when necessary – A friend or relative might have easier access to shops with a wider range of foods.

Try to keep active – Activity encourages a better appetite and therefore can lead to a wider range of foods being eaten (HN p. 298).

Remember that food provides warmth – All chemical processes in the body, including digestion, produce heat which helps to keep the body temperature at the optimum value.

Question SP13.5

The nutrients listed in HN Table 13.6 are vitamins and minerals. Table SP9.1 gives the sources of the vitamins; SP10.3.3 and 10.3.5 cover iron and zinc. Most breakfast cereals have added vitamins and minerals and regular portions would increase her intake of folate, riboflavin, thiamin and iron. Vitamin C is best obtained from fresh fruit and vegetables. Vitamin D and zinc could be obtained from additional protein, including meat, especially liver, and dairy products such as cheese and eggs.

Question SP14.1

(a) The outer layer of the wall of an artery is composed of elastin and collagen. Inside that is a layer of smooth muscle and collagen. The lumen of the artery is lined with endothelium.

(b) Both of the main layers in the wall of a vein are thinner than those in the wall of a similar sized artery (each about half as thick), and the lumen is correspondingly larger in a vein. Both are lined with endothelium. The thinner wall of a vein means that while arteries maintain their circular cross-section, veins tend to collapse under pressure from the surrounding tissues when blood is not passing through them.

Question SP14.2

(a) Atherogenesis: Turbulent blood flow and raised blood pressure lead to stress in the walls of blood vessels (especially arteries) and can cause damage to the lining. To repair the wall, extra collagen and smooth muscle are produced. These make the lining thicker and so reduce the size of the lumen and make it more difficult for the blood to pass through. The damaged wall is also more permeable, allowing substances to pass into it that would normally remain in the blood. Substances such as lipids from low density lipoproteins (LDL) pass into the wall, where they are recognised as 'foreign' (in the sense that they should not be there). They attract white blood cells called monocytes, that also penetrate the wall and become macrophages. Macrophages absorb the lipid and remain in the wall, coalescing to form foam cells. They eventually die and the fat inside them forms fatty streaks in the artery walls. Platelets and fibrin, which normally are part of the blood clotting process, arrive at the damaged area and form a fatty plaque that further constricts the lumen of the artery and prevents blood flow.

(b) Thrombogenesis: At some point, the fatty plaque breaks up and releases its fatty contents into the circulation. Platelets and fibrin collect around the fatty pieces and form clots (called thrombi; singular, thrombus). If a clot lodges in one of the coronary arteries, then the part of the heart normally supplied with oxygen by that vessel, is damaged and may die if damage is extensive. The heart is likely to stop beating (cardiac arrest), though it is often possible with medical intervention to re-start the heart, so that the person survives.

Question SP14.3

(a) Assuming that you have given each carbon atoms four bonds, your sketch should look like the one shown opposite.

(b) The description of cholesterol in SP5.4.2 says that it 'has a complex structure based on four rings of carbon atoms, three with six carbon atoms and one with five'. The sketch has these features.

(c) Typically fats have at least one long chain of carbon atoms, with hydrogen atoms attached. Triacylglycerols have three such chains (derived from the three fatty acids). A long chain of carbon atoms (with hydrogen atoms, or other carbon atoms attached) can be identified in the cholesterol molecule too. This is at least 15 carbon atoms long (depending on which way you count around the rings), and so is similar to the length of many fatty acids. It is this structure that gives cholesterol the properties of a lipid.

(d) From SP5.4.2, cholesterol is part of the structure of cell membranes. It is used in the production of bile salts and in the synthesis of various hormones, including the sex hormones, other important steroids and vitamin D.

Question SP14.4

(a) $\dfrac{P}{S} = 0.5$ could also be written as $\dfrac{P}{S} = \dfrac{1}{2}$, so there needs to be twice as much S (saturated fatty acids) in the diet as P (polyunsaturated fatty acids). So, of every three fatty acids, one should be polyunsaturated for every two saturated. Thus one-third of dietary fatty acids should be polyunsaturated.

(b) $\dfrac{P}{S} = 0.8$ could also be written as $\dfrac{P}{S} = \dfrac{8}{10}$, so for every 18 fatty acids, eight should be polyunsaturated for every 10 saturated. Thus $\dfrac{8}{18}$ or $\dfrac{4}{9}$ of the dietary fatty acids should be polyunsaturated, which is almost a half.

(c) To increase the P/S ratio, a person would need to reduce the amount of animal fats in their diet and increase their intake of oily fish, and fats derived from plant sources, such as nuts (see Table SP5.1).

Question SP14.5

HN Figure 14.5 shows the number of people in the different social classes who die from CHD, shown separately for men and women. A standardised mortality ratio of 100 is the number of people that are expected to die in a standard population. You can think of it as an 'average'. Bars above this line indicate higher than average mortality; bars below the line indicate lower average mortality. For both men and women, those in lower social classes have mortality rates higher than average and those in higher social classes have mortality rates lower than average. The distinction is more marked in women, i.e. the excess mortality rate for women in the unskilled category is higher than that for men in the same category, and similarly, the reduction in the mortality rate for professional women is greater than that for professional men.

Question SP14.6

The factors affect the risk of developing CHD as follows:

- Genetic predisposition: There is a much greater risk of developing CHD in those for whom there is a family history of heart disease.
- Age: CHD develops over time, with mortality in men highest between the ages of 55 and 64 and in women between 75 and 84.
- Social class: CHD is most common in those from lower social classes and has the lowest incidence in professional men and women.
- Birthweight: Adults who were small at birth are more likely to develop CHD, especially if they become overweight in later life.
- Geographical location: CHD is more common in northern latitudes and less common nearer the Equator, possibly due to a link with vitamin D.
- Disease: Individuals with type 2 diabetes have an increased risk of developing CHD, as do individuals with some types of infection.
- Smoking: The increased free radicals that enter the body in cigarette smoke appear to be linked to the increase in CHD in smokers.
- High blood pressure: Hypertension is one of the main contributory factors to CHD, since it damages the lining of blood vessels.

- Raised blood lipids: Raised levels of blood lipids, especially LDL and related lipoproteins, such as VLDL and chylomicrons, are strongly linked with an increased risk of developing CHD.

- Weight: The risk of developing CHD is 2–3 times greater in those with BMI greater than 30 (> 30), compared with those whose BMI is less than 25 (< 25), and the risk is particularly increased if the excess body fat is around the abdomen.

- Physical activity: Active individuals are much less likely to develop CHD.

- Psychosocial factors: Stress and lack of a good social network for support may be linked to increased CHD.

Question SP15.1

'Choose predominantly plant-based diets …' Taking the segments of the BGH plate labelled 'fruit and vegetables' and 'bread, other cereals and potatoes' as being the 'plant-based' part of the diet, then the BGH diet is predominantly (more than half) plant-based. However, the WCRF report may be intended to suggest a greater plant-based part than this. It is not possible to tell precisely. The BGH plate does include meat, fish and alternatives (many of which are plant-based) as about an eighth of the diet, which could be said to be a significant part.

'Eat 400–800 g or five or more portions a day of a variety of vegetables and fruit …' The BGH shows that more than a quarter of the diet should be composed of fruit and vegetables, and indicates that a variety would be desirable. Whether this recommendation would constitute 400–800 g, or five portions, is less easy to ascertain.

'Eat 600–800 g or more than seven portions of cereals, pulses, roots, tubers and plantains. Prefer minimally processed foods. Limit consumption of refined sugar.' Assuming that the cereals, pulses, etc. in the WCRF report is equivalent to the 'bread, other cereals and potatoes' segment in the BGH plate, then the two do not coincide. The BGH shows a similar sized segment for 'bread, other cereals and potatoes' as for 'fruit and vegetables', not half as much again as the WCRF report suggests. Processed foods and foods containing refined sugar are almost all contained in the 'food containing fat and food containing sugar' segment of the BGH plate, which is certainly the smallest segment, so the advice there is reasonably consistent.

'Alcohol consumption is not recommended.' The BGH plate does not appear to include any alcohol, but does not specifically exclude it.

'limit intake of red meat to less than 80 g daily. Choose fish [and] poultry … in place of red meat.' The BGH plate does not show quantities and appears to show various sorts of meat, not just fish and poultry.

'Limit consumption of fatty foods … Choose modest amounts of appropriate vegetable oils.' The BGH plate also suggests only a limited amount of fatty foods. It does not particularly recommend oils rather than fats. The WCRF recommendation does not make clear which vegetable oils would be 'appropriate' and which would not.

'Limit consumption of salted foods….' This is not shown on the BGH plate, so no comparison can be made.

Question SP16.1

The factors are:

- Increased resting energy expenditure – Although HIV infection may increase resting metabolic rate, patients more than compensate by a reduction in energy expenditure, and so increased BMR is not the main reason for weight loss.

- Concurrent infection – Periods of infection reduce the appetite and once the patient begins to recover, it is important to increase the intake of protein in particular.

- Reduced food intake – This occurs due to lack of appetite, inability to obtain food and problems with the processes of eating and digesting food.

- Malabsorption – HIV infection can alter the ability of the body to take up digested food from the gut.

Question SP16.2

The bar chart shows how the muscle glycogen stores (see SP6.7) vary before and after exercise, in subjects who have different amounts of carbohydrate (abbreviated to CHO) in their diet. Although there is no indication of how many subjects were in each group, we can assume that these results are the averages from a number of people. The amounts of carbohydrate eaten by the different groups are 375 g per day, 525 g per day and 650 g per day. Before exercise, the muscle glycogen levels of all subjects were about the same and within the normal range. In all three groups, the glycogen fell to just under half the original amount after exercise. When the muscle glycogen levels were checked 24 hours later, that in the muscles of the subjects who had the lowest level of carbohydrate in their diet (375 g per day) had recovered only a little, and was still well below the normal range. The muscle glycogen level in the subjects with 525 g of carbohydrate in their diet, however, had recovered almost to normal, whilst in those subjects with the highest amount of carbohydrate in their diet (650 g per day), the muscle glycogen levels had not only recovered but had risen to the top of the normal range, slightly greater than their starting level.

The conclusion is that athletes needing to exercise on a daily basis should have a diet rich in carbohydrate. The actual amount needed will depend on the intensity and duration of their training. *(253 words)*

Question SP16.3

(a) Energy from carbohydrate needed by the athlete per day

$$= 60\% \text{ of } 21 \text{ MJ}$$

$$= \frac{60}{100} \times 21 \times 1000 \text{ kJ}$$

$$= 12\,600 \text{ kJ}$$

From Table SP7.1, the energy yield of carbohydrates is about 17 kJ per gram.

So, amount of carbohydrate required to generate 12 600 kJ $= \dfrac{12600}{17}$ g $= 741$ g

(b) To obtain 741 g of carbohydrate from a food that is 17% carbohydrate, would require the consumption of 741 g $\times \dfrac{100}{17} = 4359$ g, which is over 4 kg of potatoes!

(c) To obtain 741 g carbohydrate from baked beans would mean eating 7410 g. One tin contains 420 g, so 7410 g would be nearly 18 tins of baked beans. Since each tin contains about 280 calories, that would supply about the 5000 kcal required each day, but would not constitute a balanced diet, and is certainly not to be recommended!

Question SP16.4

The glycaemic index of foods is a measure of how quickly glucose is released into the blood during digestion. Foods with a low glycaemic index release glucose more slowly into the blood, and so, for a given quantity of food, it is longer before the person feels hungry again. They are therefore likely to eat less and so may lose weight. An athlete after exercise, on the other hand, needs to refill their depleted stocks of muscle glycogen as quickly as possible, by eating foods that have a high glycaemic index and release quickly a lot of glucose into the bloodstream, which can then be converted into glycogen.

Question SP16.5

(a) Excess alcohol intake affects all three stages. It can affect food intake because of a reduced appetite, pain or nausea on eating, and difficulties of access to nutritional food because of homelessness or lack of money. It can affect food processing in the gut because alcohol is an irritant and can cause vomiting and diarrhoea. Alcohol affects the production of digestive enzymes and not all food taken in may be properly digested. It affects the utilisation of food mainly due to damage to the liver, which is important in processing fat, carbohydrate and protein. Both the liver and the pancreas, which can also be damaged, play roles in the utilisation of carbohydrate.

(b) Impairment of muscular control can have a major effect on the intake stage of the process. There may be problems with purchasing and preparing food, with transferring the food to the mouth and with chewing and swallowing. The processing and utilisation steps may be less affected, though the drugs a person is taking to control their condition may have side-effects on those stages too.

Question SP17.1

There is a legal framework in the UK that separates foods and medicines and does not allow foods to be described as having a particular health benefit. Drugs have gone through a rigorous testing regime, including on animals, before clinical trials (using people) begin and studies must also have been done on the exact biochemical effect of the drug in the body. Generally, foods have been tested much less rigorously. However, where a health claim is made for a new food product, scientific evidence is now being collected. The intention is that the food should be tested in a similar way to a drug, including human trials, safety assessments and dose–response relationships. Drugs can be prescribed in measured doses, but if a particular beneficial chemical is included in food, it is unlikely to be possible to ensure that a person eats a particular amount of that food. The active ingredient may be present in a number of foods that the person might include in their diet. So, it is particularly important to ensure that there are no adverse effects resulting from large intakes of the ingredient. (*187 words*)

Question SP17.2

(a) In a natural fat molecule, the substance that the fatty acids are attached to is glycerol. Each glycerol molecule can bond with three fatty acid molecules to form a triacylglycerol. When the bond forms, one hydrogen (H) from an OH group in the glycerol combines with an OH group from the fatty acid, linking them together and releasing a molecule of water (H_2O) (Figure SP5.2).

(b) Since each fatty acid needs to link with the H of an OH group on the sucrose, the number of fatty acids that can link to a sucrose molecule depends on the number of OH groups it has. Figure SP17.1 shows that a sucrose molecule has nine OH groups, and therefore theoretically could link to nine fatty acids. In fact, Olestra is a mix of sucrose molecules with six, seven and eight fatty acids attached.

(c) Fats are digested by the enzyme lipase, which splits off two fatty acids, leaving a monoacylglycerol. Both the individual fatty acids and the monoacylglycerol are then small enough to pass into the cells lining the digestive system (the epithelium), where they are reassembled and then passed into the bloodstream (Figure SP5.9). You may have realised from your reading of Part Two, that enzymes are quite specific, that is, a particular enzyme works on a particular type of molecule, and only that type. Thus it would be reasonable to hypothesise that the lipase, which works on triacylglycerols, is unlikely to work on a synthetic fat like Olestra, containing a sucrose molecule rather than a glycerol, leaving intact Olestra molecules that would be too big to pass through into the epithelial cells of the digestive system. Thus they would remain in the digestive system to be eliminated in the faeces. This situation happens and the additional fatty substances in the faeces often cause diarrhoea. The consumption of large quantities of Olestra can lead to excessive losses of water and minerals from the body and is one of the reasons why the substance has not been licensed for use in Europe.

Question SP17.3

(a) Functional foods are those foods that are considered by some to have health-promoting benefits in addition to their usual nutritional value, e.g. vegetables contain phytochemicals. Fortified foods are a type of functional food. They have added nutrients, often vitamins, that would not normally be found in the food. For example, vitamins A and D are added to margarine and similar spreads, since they would not normally occur there, whereas they do occur in butter, which the spreads might replace.

(b) Vitamins are chemicals found in a range of foods and are required in only very small amounts in the diet. A recognised deficiency syndrome occurs if a particular vitamin is absent from the diet; for example, lack of vitamin C results in the symptoms of scurvy. Vitamins can be found in foods derived from both animals and plants. Phytochemicals, on the other hand, are found only in plants and food products made from plants. They are produced by the plant as a defence mechanism and generally do not have a pleasant taste. However, high intake of phytochemicals appears to be linked to lower rates of cancer and coronary heart disease. Phytochemicals include phenolic compounds such as flavonoids, phyto-oestrogens, glucosinolates and carotenoids.

(c) Probiotics are food products that contain live microbes. The intention is that these microbes establish themselves in the gut and improve the balance of the intestinal microbes. Such microbes are important for the breakdown of some food and are thought to contribute 7–10% of the body's daily energy needs (HN Figure 17.2. They also seem to provide some protection against chronic inflammatory diseases and allergies. It is important that the microbes have appropriate substances to use as their nutrient source, and these substances are called prebiotics. They are non-digestible food components, such as oligosaccharides containing fructose, that are found in a range of foods such as dairy products, infant formula and bakery products.

Question SP17.4

There is as yet no clear evidence that organic foods, grown by traditional methods without the use of artificial fertilisers, pesticides, etc., have a higher nutrient content. Conventionally produced vegetables do appear to have a lower vitamin C content, probably because they contain more water and therefore the vitamin C is more diluted. They also contain more nitrate than organic vegetables, though there is no evidence that this feature has any impact on health. Organic foods may have higher levels of phytochemicals, which appear to have health benefits, since they are used by the plants for protective purposes and may be produced in greater quantities in crops not protected by chemical sprays. On the other hand, due to the application of manure, organic crops could have a higher level of contamination from disease-causing microbes. Much of the organic food on sale in supermarkets has been imported, and so may be less fresh than local non-organic fruit and vegetables, with the possibility that nutrients have been lost during transport. As yet, then, there is little direct evidence that organic foods are 'better for you' than more conventionally grown crops and they are likely to be more expensive.

Question SP18.1

(a) The dietary factors are:

- Macronutrients: *n*-3 fatty acids
- Vitamins: folate, vitamin D, C
- Minerals: calcium, potassium, fluoride
- Other micronutrients: antioxidants
- Foods: dietary fibre (NSP), fruit and vegetables, dairy products

(b) The oily fish would provide the *n*-3 fatty acids and the vitamin D. Folate is present in a variety of vegetables and some fruit. Calcium would be obtained from some oily fish, e.g. sardines whose bones are eaten, and is also present in green leafy vegetables. Potassium is present in bananas and in vegetables. Vitamins A and C which would be plentiful in this diet are antioxidants. Dietary fibre would be present in the fruit and vegetables. So the only item not covered is 'dairy products'.

Question SP18.2

(a) Physical activity level, $\text{PAL} = \dfrac{\text{total energy expenditure}}{\text{resting energy expenditure}}$

PAL > 1.75 means that the goal is for people to be taking sufficient exercise to raise their PAL to over 1.75, equivalent to more than 30 minutes walking per day.

(b) For all the fatty acids except *n*-3 PUFAs (polyunsaturated fatty acids), the amounts are given as percentages of the total energy available in the diet; for example, there should be less than 2% of *trans* fatty acids and about 10–15% of MUFAs (monounsaturated fatty acids). The *n*-3 PUFAs are given as weights, i.e. 2 g linoleic (acid) and 200 mg of very long chain PUFAs. It must be assumed (though the table does not make it clear) that the values are suggested daily intakes. Since these values are very small amounts compared with the intakes of the other fatty acids, if they were given as a percentage they would appear as well under 1%. So, since the authors of the Eurodiet Core Report wanted to emphasise their importance, the *n*-3 PUFA values have been presented differently.

(c) The optimum values for alcohol intake are the lower values, i.e. 24 g for men and 12 g for women. Since a standard 'unit' of alcohol (ethanol) is 8 g, then the recommended quantity is equivalent to 3 units for men and 1.5 units for women. Alcohol appears to provide some protection against CHD, but the optimum amount is about 1–2 units per day (see HN p. 52 and p. 318), so the values in HN Table 18.2 are slightly higher than this.

(d) Dietary fibre intake is given as >25 g per day, or 3 g/MJ. 1 MJ (megajoule) is 1000 kJ (kilojoules). So 1 MJ would be about 250 kcal (or Calories). Typical daily energy intakes are given as 2500 kcal for men and 2000 kcal for women (HN p. 46), or about 10 MJ for men and 8 MJ for women. So the inclusion of 3 g of fibre for each MJ of energy consumed, would indicate 30 g fibre for men and 24 g for women, close to the 25 g value given. It is not easy to measure a person's dietary fibre (NSP) intake, since it is normally taken in as an integral part of foods such as fruit and vegetables; hence the advice to eat more portions of these items, rather than to take in at least 25 g of fibre per day.

(e) The value for fruit and vegetables is given as grams per day, and for folate as micrograms (μg) per day. There are 1000 μg in a milligram (mg) and 1000 mg in a gram, so the value for folate intake is actually a million times smaller than the fruit and vegetable value.

Question SP18.3

(a) Targeting those individuals who are at the highest risk certainly benefits those individuals, as long as they take the advice. However, overall, those individuals are only a relatively small percentage of the population as a whole. There is a much larger percentage of the population, maybe most of the population, who are at moderate risk and who could benefit by taking healthy eating advice aimed at everyone. So the overall population's risk of death and illness (mortality and morbidity) from preventable conditions would be reduced much more by advice to everyone. (HN pp. 384–5)

(b) It is much more difficult to follow advice that is nutrient-based, e.g. see Question SP18.2d. For instance, it is generally not helpful to be advised to eat more than 25 g of dietary fibre per day. It is much easier for people to understand advice based on foods, e.g. eat five portions of fruit and vegetables per day. (HN p. 385)

Acknowledgements

The Course Team would like to thank Caroline Pond for her helpful comments on the course materials.

Grateful acknowledgement is made to the following sources for permission to reproduce material within this product.

Frontispiece and *Figure SP3.2*: Copyright © Food Standards Agency; *Figure SP1.2a*: Biophoto Associates; *Figure SP1.2b*: CRC Institute of Cancer Studies, University of Birmingham; *Figure SP1.3*: Andrew Syred/Science Photo Library; *Figure SP4.9a*: Eye of Science/Science Photo Library; *Figure SP5.9*: Adapted from Vander, A. J., Sherman, J. H. and Lucian, D. S. (1994) *Human Physiology*, Sixth International Edition, copyright © 1994, 1990, 1985,1980,1975,1970 by McGraw-Hill, Inc.; *Figure SP6.6.b*: Eye of Science/Science Photo Library; *Figure SP8.1*: Bender, D. A. (1993) *An Introduction to Nutrition and Metabolism*, Taylor and Francis; *Figure SP9.2*: Biophoto Associates/Science Photo Library; *Figure SP10.1*: Source unknown; *Figure SP10.2*: Van Wynsberghe, D., Noback, C. R. and Carola, R. (1995) *Human Anatomy and Physiology*, 3rd edn, McGraw-Hill, Inc., by permission of The McGraw-Hill Companies; *Figure SP14.3*: Grundy, S. M. (1986) *Journal of the American Medical Association*, vol. 256, 1986. American Medical Association; *Figure SP15.1*: Produced by the Department of Health, © Crown copyright 2003.

Every effort has been made to contact copyright holders. If any have been inadvertently overlooked, the publishers will be pleased to make the necessary arrangements at the first opportunity.

Index

Page numbers in *italics* refer to figures or tables.